AF782674

FOCUS ON CHEMISTRY AND BIOCHEMISTRY

FOCUS ON CHEMISTRY AND BIOCHEMISTRY

GUENNADI E. ZAIKOV, VICTOR M.M. LOBO
AND NEKANE GUARROTXENA
(EDITORS)

Nova Science Publishers, Inc.
New York

Senior Editors: Susan Boriotti and Donna Dennis
Coordinating Editor: Tatiana Shohov
Office Manager: Annette Hellinger
Graphics: Wanda Serrano
Editorial Production: Maya Columbus, Vladimir Klestov, Matthew Kozlowski, and Tom Moceri
Circulation: Ave Maria Gonzalez, Vera Popovic, Luis Aviles, Raymond Davis, Melissa Diaz, Magdalene Nunez, Marlene Nunez and Jeannie Pappas
Communications and Acquisitions: Serge P. Shohov
Marketing: Cathy DeGregory

Library of Congress Cataloging-in-Publication Data
Available Upon Request

ISBN: 1-59033-596-1.

Copyright © 2003 by Nova Science Publishers, Inc.
400 Oser Ave, Suite 1600
Hauppauge, New York 11788-3619
Tele. 631-231-7269 Fax 631-231-8175
e-mail: Novascience@earthlink.net
Web Site: http://www.novapublishers.com

All rights reserved. No part of this book may be reproduced, stored in a retrieval system or transmitted in any form or by any means: electronic, electrostatic, magnetic, tape, mechanical photocopying, recording or otherwise without permission from the publishers.

The authors and publisher have taken care in preparation of this book, but make no expressed or implied warranty of any kind and assume no responsibility for any errors or omissions. No liability is assumed for incidental or consequential damages in connection with or arising out of information contained in this book.

This publication is designed to provide accurate and authoritative information with regard to the subject matter covered herein. It is sold with the clear understanding that the publisher is not engaged in rendering legal or any other professional services. If legal or any other expert assistance is required, the services of a competent person should be sought. FROM A DECLARATION OF PARTICIPANTS JOINTLY ADOPTED BY A COMMITTEE OF THE AMERICAN BAR ASSOCIATION AND A COMMITTEE OF PUBLISHERS.

Printed in the United States of America

CONTENTS

PREFACE

"We can divide people into 2 groups: those who prefer it and those who have never tried it."
Advertisement for Premium Scotch Whisky (Chivas Regal) at Moscow International Airport "Sheremet'evo"

We can probably say the same about chemical and biochemical physics: once having learned about them you will never part with this field of science.

Now a little English joke. Students in boats from Cambridge and Oxford Universities are sailing along the Thames-river. Suddenly they see a man who is swimming across the Thames fully dressed in a suit, in a shirt and with his shoes on. One of the students asks: "Why are you swimming in such a strange way?", and the man answers them: "You are sailing and I am drowning". Unfortunately we can compare the students in the boats with American and West European science and the man who is drowning with Russian Science. What is surprising is that Russian science has been drowning for 10 years and has not drowned yet. The articles of Russian contributors included in this book, in our opinion, are confirmation of this.

We think that this book will be useful for scientists who are working in the field of pure and applied chemistry.

Volume Editors
Prof. Guennadi E. Zaikov
N.M. Emanuel Institute of Biochemical Physics
Russian Academy of Sciences, 4, Kosygin str., Moscow 119991, Russia

Prof. Victor M.M. Lobo
Coimbra University, Chemical Department
Coimbra-Center, Portugal – 3000

Dr. Nekane Guarrotxena
Institute of Science and Engineering of Polymers
Madrid, Spain

AUTHOR INDEX

INDEX OF INSTITUTES

1. Coimbra University, Coimbra, Portugal – 1, 2
2. N.M. Emanuel Institute of Biochemical Physics, Russian Academy of Sciences, Moscow, Russia – 1, 3, 5, 6, 9
3. Universite de Libre de Brussell, Brussel, Belgium – 1
4. A.N.Nesmeyanov Institute of Organoelement Compounds, Russian Academy of Sciences, Moscow, Russia – 4
5. Pisarevskii Institute of Physical Chemistry, L'viv Department of Ukraine Academy of Sciences, L'viv, Ukraine – 5, 6
6. Donetsk State University, Donetsk, Ukraine – 5, 6
7. Karpenko Physico-Mechanical Institute, Ukraine Academy of Sciences, L'viv, Ukraine – 5, 6
8. Commercial Academy, L'viv, Ukraine – 5, 6
9. Institute of Organic Chemistry, Ufa Scientifical Center of Russian Academy of Sciences, Ufa, Russia – 7
10. Scientific Research Institute "Syntez", Moscow - 8

Chapter 1

INTEGRAL DIFFUSION COEFFICIENTS OF SYMMETRICAL 1:1 STRONG ELECTROLYTES IN WATER SWOLLEN ACRYLAMIDE-BASED HYDROGELS

A.J.M. Valente, A.Ya. Polishchuk[†], V.M.M. Lobo and G. Geuskens[††]

Department of Chemistry, University of Coimbra, 3004-535 Coimbra, Portugal.
avalente@ci.uc.pt, vlobo@ci.uc.pt.

[†] Kompamid LLC, 18 Bazhova Street, Moscow 129128, Russia.
polishchuk@kompamid.ru.

[††] Department of Macromolecular Chemistry, Free University of Brussels, Campus Plaine, CP206/1, B-1050 Brussels, Belgium. geuskens@ ulb.ac.be.

ABSTRACT

Diffusion of non-associated electrolytes (potassium chloride and lithium chloride) in concentrated aqueous solutions (0.1 M to 1.0 M) has been studied in hydrogels derived from acrylamide and methyl methacrylate to study the mechanism of electrolyte transport. The preparation of two gels with different monomer ratio compositions resulted in obtaining membranes of substantially different hydrophilic character with polymer fractions of 0.3 and 0.5.

Free Volume Cukier hydrodynamic models were applied to explain the dependence of the diffusion coefficients of KCl and LiCl on the electrolyte concentration in hydrogel obtained experimentally. It was shown that the increase of the diffusion coefficients is accompanied with a decrease of the mean distance of approach of the ions. This can be explained by the formation of ion-pairs, resulting in a further contribution to diffusion once there is a decrease in the hydrodynamic resistance of the medium to the diffusing particles. Parameters, which characterise such behaviour quantitatively, are different for different electrolytes and depend on water content in the gel.

Key Words: Diffusion Coefficients; Hydrogels; Acrylamide; Methylmethacrylate; Water; Electrolytes.

INTRODUCTION

Polymer gels are important materials of both fundamental and technological applications. Consequently hydrogels are widely used as specific sorbents in different fields [1-5].

It is well known that the swelling behaviour of polymer gels and their physical properties depend on the network structure. Although extensive work has been reported for the transport of materials in hydrogels, only a few dealt with the diffusion of strong electrolytes. At the same time the role of diffusion processes in many industrial applications of hydrogels accounts for the increasing interest in this area. Consequently there is a need in finding a tool to control the diffusion and obtain the desirable diffusion characteristics.

The hydrophilic character of acrylamide hydrogels depends on the concentration of the cross-linker [6]. However, the possibility of altering the material hydrophilicity using this property is severely limited. An alternative way for controlling the hydrophilic/hydrophobic balance in polyacrylamide-based hydrogels, is the design of co-polymers containing hydrophobic monomers. The scope of this paper is an investigation of the effect of a specific co-monomer, the methyl methacrylate on the transport of non-associated electrolytes (KCl and LiCl) in acrylamide-based gels in comparison with the isolated effect of cross-linker.

EXPERIMENTAL

Reagents

The chemicals are from the following sources: acrylamide (AAm) and methylmethacrylate (MMA) from Riedel-de Häen; N,N'-methylene-bis-acrylamide (MBAAm) from Merck; sodium persulphate from Fluka AG; poly(vinyl alcohol) (PVA) of molecular weight of 13,000–23,000 from Aldrich Co.; lithium chloride and potassium chloride from Riedel-de Häen (these electrolytes were further dried until constant weight at 110 °C (KCl) and 180 °C (LiCl) [7]); 2-propanol from Riedel-de Häen; tri-distilled water from our laboratory. All chemicals were of *Pro-Analysis* quality and used without further purification.

Synthesis

The hydrogel membranes were produced polymerising (by free radical polymerisation [8]) the pre-gel homogeneous solution (Table 1) inside two glass sheets separated by a plastic rubber gasket. The initiator was added to all pre-gel solutions in the concentration of 1 % (wt/v). The addition of PVA in gel IV is due to increase the mechanical strength of the membrane. Spring clips were used to hold the glass sheets together. After this procedure, the mould was placed in an oven at 50 °C for 2 hours. The hydrogel membrane was then removed from the mould, placed between two plastic sheets, and stored inside an exsiccator at nearly 100% humidity.

Table 1. Composition of the pre-gel solutions.

Hydrogel	AAm / v %	MMA* / v %	MBAAm / (mol/mol %)	PVA / (wt/v %)
I	100	0	1	-
II	100	0	5	-
III	80	20	5	-
IV	60	40	5	0.05 – 0.1

AAm = acrylamide; MMA = methylmethacrylate; MBAAm = N,N'-methylene-bis-acrylamide; PVA = poly(vinyl alchool). * The MMA was dissolved in 1-propanol.

Equilibrium Studies

Different samples of the same membranes were cut, weighed (w_i) and immersed in water until equilibrium was reached. When the hydrogel samples reach the equilibrium in water, they were transferred from water to each of the salt solutions, from 0.1 M to 1.0 M, with a volume V_{sol}, and left to reach equilibrium (14 days). The equilibrium time in both experiments were approximately 2 weeks. After this time, the membranes were removed and weighed, w_{eq}. The approach to equilibrium was controlled gravimetically (Sartorius analytical balance, with a resolution of 0.1 mg) and when necessary the volume of the swollen membrane, V, was measured.

The swelling degree of the gel, Q, in salt (water and aqueous salt) solutions is calculated from

$$Q = w_{eq} / w_0 \quad (1)$$

where w_0 is the weight of the xerogel calculated considering the complete conversion of the solutes and solvents during polymerisation [9].

The concentration of a specific electrolyte sorbed by the membrane (C_{eq}) was calculated by measuring the concentration of salt in the aqueous solution prior to (c_0) and after (c_∞) the swelling experiments, using a conductivity instrument (YSI 3200), according to

$$C_{eq} = (c_\infty - c_0)\, V / V_p \quad (2)$$

where V and V_p are the volume of the aqueous solution and membrane sample, respectively.

Each experiment was repeated at least 3 times and they were carried out at 25 °C.

Permeability Cell

The same permeability cell was used to measure the steady-state flux (*J*) of the electrolyte through hydrogel membranes, which was earlier designed, and described in the references [10, 11]. Basically, the cell consists of two compartments of 250 mL each, connected by two horizontal tubes of 14 mm diameter. The polymeric membrane, previously swollen in water up to the equilibrium, is sealed with silicone between these two tubes thus separating compartments, of which one is initially filled with electrolyte solution and the other with water. The electrolyte flux was monitored using a selective chloride electrode coupled with a pH Meter Methrom 645, with a 0.1 mV resolution. The temperature remained constant throughout the permeability experiments (thermostatic bath Multistirrer 6 from Velp Scientifica) and the solutions were stirred at ca. 220 rpm in both cells.

The initial concentration of electrolyte solution is in the range 0.1-1.0 M. For each of these initial concentrations, the electrolyte concentration inside the membrane (C_{eq}) was calculated. This is taken as the concentration at the interface between the membrane and electrolyte solution. Each C_{eq} value was simply found using results of sorption experiments. The integral diffusion coefficient of the electrolyte in a gel, D_F, was then calculated from

$$D_F = J\, l \,/\, C_{eq} \qquad (3)$$

for different c values, where l is the thickness of the hydrogel membrane, measured after each experiment, and J is the steady-state flux.

Results and Discussion

Sorption Isotherms

Figure 1 shows the sorption isotherms of KCl (black points) and LiCl (white points) in the different hydrogels.

All sorption isotherms experimental data fits reasonable well with the equation

$$C = C_L\, K_L\, c \,/\, (1 + K_L\, c) \qquad (4)$$

where C and c are the electrolyte concentration inside and outside polymer, respectively, C_L is the concentration of the electrolyte molecules that could be sorbed due to interaction with polar groups of the polymer at saturation conditions, and K_L is the corresponding equilibrium constant.

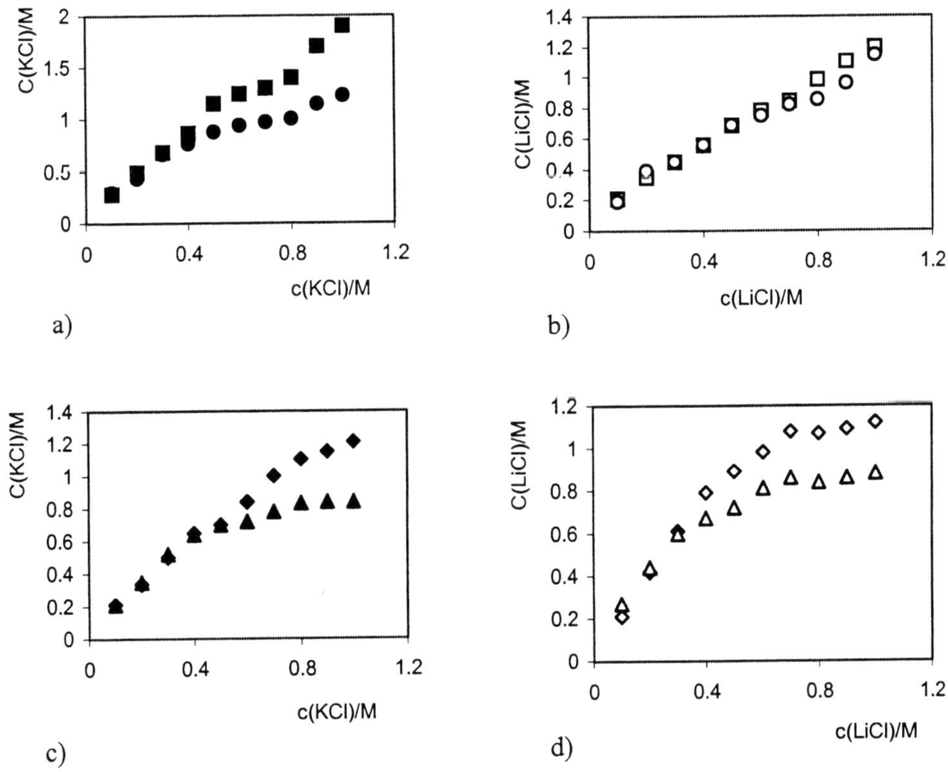

Figure 1. Sorption isotherms of KCl (black points) and LiCl (white points) in: (a) gel I; (b) gel II; (c) gel III; (d) gel IV.

Table 2 shows the fitting parameters of the experimental data using eq. (4). From the analysis of these data we may conclude that the effect of the cross-linker in the polyacrylamides (gels I and II) is higher in the KCl systems – the values of C_L and K_L to LiCl systems are approximately the same. This can be justified by the highly stabilised ion-water and ion-ion (ion-pair formation) interactions that characterise the Li^+ aqueous solutions. This is a consequence of the high charge density of the lithium ion as well as of the positive hydration [12]. The opposite effect produced by potassium ions on the water structure is characterised by a water-breaker structure. It may justify the dependence of C on c in these two gels, and the values of C_L and K_L may be justified by the balance between the ion-pair formation at higher KCl concentrations [13], and the water-breaker structure features of the potassium ions lower concentrations. The latter feature results in water-water and possible ion-polymer interactions predominance in comparison with ion-water interactions. That balance is enhanced (higher K_L) by the decrease of water concentration in the gel II. These results also clearly suggest that the hydrolysis of the amide groups of polyacrylamide [14] may occur. We also may see that to the highest KCl concentrations in gel I there is a slightly increase of C with c suggesting a tendency for a distribution coefficient to increase which can be explained by a possible increase in ion-ion interaction.

Table 2. Langmuir's parameters computed from fitting eq. (4) to the experimental data shown in sorption isotherms (Fig. 1).

	KCl solutions				LiCl solutions			
	gel I	gel II	gel III	gel IV	gel I	gel II	gel IIII	gel IV
C_L / M	3.7	1.7	2.3	1.5	1.8	1.9	3.2	1.3
K_L	0.8	2.0	0.5	1.7	1.3	1.1	0.7	2.7
R^2	0.99	0.98	0.99	0.99	0.99	0.99	0.99	1.00

To gels III and IV, eq. (4) can be written considering the contribution of AAm and MMA monomers, assuming that the effect of these monomers in the sorption process is different. Thus, in general, sorption of an electrolyte can be described by equations

$$C_{eq} = [C_{L1} K_{L1} c /(1 + K_{L1} c)] + [C_{L2} K_{L2} c /(1 + K_{L2} c)] \quad (5)$$

where C_{L1} is the concentration of the electrolyte molecules that could be sorbed due to interaction with, say, acrylamide groups at saturation conditions, K_{L1} is the corresponding equilibrium constant, C_{L2} and K_{L2} are parameters characterising electrolyte interaction with methylmethacrylate.

From eqs. (4) and (5) we find that $C_L = C_{L1} C_{L2} /(C_{L1} + C_{L2})$ and $K_L = K_{L1} K_{L2} (C_{L1} + C_{L2})/(K_{L1}C_{L1} + K_{L2} C_{L2})$ are effective (or average) parameters of an electrolyte sorption by co-polymer.

Table 2 shows that C_L decreases and K_L increase with the increase of the concentration of MMA-groups in the co-polymer. It is quite reasonable that more hydrophobic MMA sorbs less amount of electrolyte from aqueous solution than AAm, and therefore gel III is characterised by a lower C_L value than that of gel IV. Furthermore, it is reported [15] that methylmethacrylate should make the access of the electrolyte to the hydrated water molecules of the remaining polar groups of the gel more difficult, due to the steric hindrance. This effect is also clear in the system KCl/gel I. For this reason the contribution of AAm and MMA monomers in electrolyte sorption is not additive as it is proved by C_L data shown in Table 2.

An increase of the hydrophobic part of the network structure provokes a structure promotion to the water molecule [16]. In these circumstances the specific features of an electrolyte affect the stability of water molecules to a lesser degree. Consequently, the solubility of both electrolytes becomes similar as measured for C_L values of KCl and LiCl in gel IV. This is not the case of gel III, where the predominant hydrophilic acrylamide groups are typically non-aqueous [16]. In this case, water structure promotion is provoked by the lithium ions only, whereas potassium ions have the structure-breaker effect on the water molecules [12]. This can explain higher solubility of LiCl in gel III in comparison with that of KCl.

Diffusion Coefficients

Tables 3 and 4 show the integral diffusion coefficients, D_F, of KCl and LiCl in the different acrylamide-based hydrogels [17,18].

The Fickian diffusion coefficients of the electrolytes are only one order of magnitude lower than in aqueous solutions [19], and the D_F dependence on electrolyte concentration is similar to that occurring in aqueous solution. In a first approach, the D_F as a function of the electrolyte concentration, C, inside gel I, is similar to that in free solution: the D_F(KCl) is higher than D_F(LiCl). The increasing hydration radius of the lithium ions and the decreasing K^+ hydration radius due to the hydrophilic character of the matrix, as pointed out before [20 (pp.96)] can justify this fact. Another evidence is that D_F increases with the electrolyte concentration. This phenomenon may be interpreted as a consequence of electrolyte ion-pair formation [20]. This also suggests that the water inside gel have an important role in the diffusion mechanism in this gel once enhance the ion-ion and ion-water interactions. However, inside gel II D_F(LiCl) > D_F (KCl). The high charge density of lithium may promote the ion-pair formation [21], predominant when the water concentration decreases and, consequently, the diffusion coefficients increase once, as a rule, the hydrodynamic resistance of the medium to one particle is smaller than the total resistance to solvated ions.

Table 3. Fickian diffusion coefficients, D_F, of KCl in acrylamide-based hydrogels, at 25°C.

c / M	Gel I	Gel II	Gel III	Gel IV
	D_F (± s) / (10^{-10} m^2 s^{-1})			
0.1	5.1 (± 1.5)	2.6 (± 0.3)	4.57 (± 0.41)	1.77 (± 0.09)
0.2	5.2 (± 0.2)	3.1 (± 0.2)	4.82 (± 0.22)	1.89 (± 0.06)
0.3	5.5 (± 0.3)	3.2 (± 0.5)	5.40 (± 0.16)	2.02 (± 0.04)
0.4	5.7 (± 0.3)	3.9 (± 0.3)	5.45 (± 0.23)	2.25 (± 0.08)
0.5	5.8 (± 0.5)	4.5 (± 0.1)	5.50 (± 0.31)	2.86 (± 0.06)
0.6	6.3 (± 0.4)	4.7 (± 0.1)	5.76 (± 0.39)	3.01 (± 0.04)
0.7	6.7 (± 1.0)	5.0 (± 0.4)	5.88 (± 0.22)	3.32 (± 0.07)
0.8	7.6 (± 0.3)	5.1 (± 0.3)	6.11 (± 0.18)	3.49 (± 0.07)
0.9	8.0 (± 0.4)	5.4 (± 0.2)	6.48 (± 0.08)	3.55 (± 0.04)
1.0	8.4 (± 1.1)	5.7 (± 0.5)	6.86 (± 0.10)	3.69 (± 0.08)

s is the standard deviation of the mean.

Table 4. Fickian diffusion coefficients, D_F, of LiCl in acrylamide-based hydrogels, at 25°C.

c / M	Gel I	Gel II	Gel III	Gel IV
	D_F (± s) / (10^{-10} m^2 s^{-1})			
0.1	3.65 (± 0.08)	3.6 (± 0.1)	3.14 (± 0.18)	1.41 (± 0.08)
0.2	4.8 (± 0.2)	4.7 (± 0.3)	3.25 (± 0.22)	1.52 (± 0.05)
0.3	5.1 (± 0.4)	6.3 (± 0.6)	3.44 (± 0.23)	1.60 (± 0.10)
0.4	5.3 (± 0.1)	6.5 (± 0.1)	3.58 (± 0.18)	1.67 (± 0.09)
0.5	5.6 (± 0.4)	6.6 (± 0.4)	3.71 (± 0.30)	1.88 (± 0.08)
0.6	5.9 (± 0.3)	6.7 (± 0.2)	3.96 (± 0.40)	1.99 (± 0.09)
0.7	6.5 (± 0.1)	7.2 (± 0.1)	4.02 (± 0.09)	2.28 (± 0.06)
0.8	6.7 (± 0.1)	7.4 (± 0.1)	4.30 (± 0.12)	2.46 (± 0.08)
0.9	6.9 (± 0.2)	7.6 (± 0.1)	4.75 (± 0.41)	2.78 (± 0.09)
1.0	7.2 (± 1.3)	7.7 (± 0.3)	5.00 (± 0.35)	2.95 (± 0.08)

s is the standard deviation of the mean.

Theoretical Approach

Although different models [22-24] have been developed to describe the diffusion processes of small solutes in highly hydrophilic polymer the free volume and the hydrodynamic theories are the most widely used theories for predicting diffusion coefficients in highly hydrophilic polymers [25].

In the free volume model the diffusion coefficients of the solute, in aqueous solution, inside polymer, D_F, can be expressed as

$$D_F / D_0 = k_1 \exp (-k_2 r_s^2 \varphi / (1 - \varphi)] \quad (6)$$

where D_0 is the diffusion coefficient of the electrolyte in aqueous solution [19], φ is the polymer volume fraction and r_s is the solute radius. Since the ions of different charge diffuse with the same velocity of the system (due to electroneutrality), r_s corresponds to a mean distance of approach of the ions. k_1 and k_2 are some undefined structural constants.

On the other hand the hydrodynamic model developed by Cukier [26] describes the dependence of diffusion coefficients of solutes (D_F) on the polymer volume fraction (φ) by

$$D_F = D_0 \exp (- k_c r_s \varphi^{0.75}) \quad (7)$$

where k_c is a constant parameter characterising specific polymer-solvent system, and r_s is the radius of the solute.

The polymer volume fractions were calculated using [25]

$$\varphi = \{1 + [(Q - 1) \rho_p / d]\}^{-1} \quad (8)$$

assuming that all sorbed electrolyte has a density, d, similar to that in aqueous solutions [27]. The polymer densities, ρ_p, of gels I to IV are 0.36 (± 0.03), 0.24 (± 0.01), 0.55 (± 0.03) and 0.53 (± 0.01) g cm^{-3}, respectively. These values were calculated assuming water density in the gels equal to 1 g cm^{-3}. The swelling degrees of the gel, Q = mass of hydrogel/mass of xerogel, are shown in the Table 5 as function of electrolyte concentration.

The application of the above models was made taken into account that in these systems water-ion (or water-electrolyte) and water-water interactions exist and water-polymer interactions cannot be neglected because these hydrogels are characterised by a very inhomogeneous monomer density [28], resulting in the existence of polymer-solvent and pure solvent regions inside the matrix.

Figure 2 shows reasonable fitting of the experimental data with eq. (6). Parameters involved in this equation were deduced using linear regression ln (D_F / D_0) vs [φ / (1 - φ)], and the results of this treatment are reported in Table 6.

Table 5. Degree of swelling (Q) for polyacrylamide-based hydrogels in aqueous KCl and LiCl solutions at 25 °C.

	gel I		gel II		gel III		gel IV	
c/M	KCl	LiCl	KCl	LiCl	KCl	LiCl	KCl	LiCl
0	12.5	12.7	5.80	5.75	5.12	5.24	3.00	3.12
0.1	12.7	12.9	5.86	5.80	5.19	5.31	3.00	3.12
0.3	13.1	13.5	5.99	5.91	5.27	5.36	3.01	3.13
0.5	13.5	14.0	6.11	6.01	5.33	5.38	3.00	3.12
0.7	14.0	14.5	6.23	6.11	5.35	5.40	2.98	3.11
1	14.6	15.3	6.42	6.27	5.37	5.41	2.97	3.11

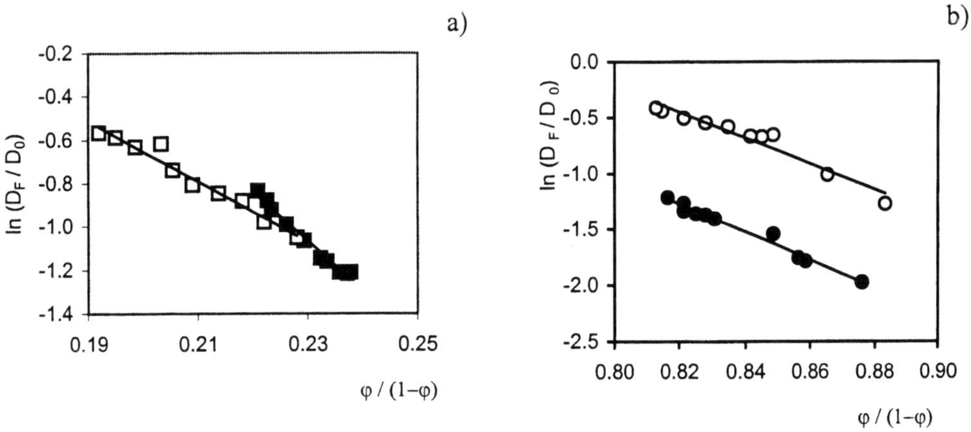

Figure 2 - Application of the free volume model, eq. (6), to the Fickian diffusion coefficients of KCl (black points) and LiCl (white points) in: (a) gel I; (b) gel II.

The dependence of electrolyte diffusion coefficient on water concentration in the polymer matrix can be expected, whereas the explanation of values shown in Table 5 requires further discussion. The eq. (6) introduces a parameter – the solute radius (r_s)- that deserves a detailed analysis, especially because we are talking about concentrated electrolyte aqueous solutions. The diffusing media is clearly aqueous. For this reason, ion-ion, ion-water and water-water interactions, as pointed out before, may have significant contributions to the diffusion mechanism. As a consequence, although the electrolyte may be assumed as an independent kinetic body (hydrated), an experimental difficulty arises with respect to determination of the r_S. This comes from the fact that the mean distance of approach of the ions, *a*, depends on the concentration [13, 30]. The value of *a* can change from the sum of the hydrated ion radii to a limit value equal to the sum of crystallographic radii, when the ions collapse forming an ion-pair. If this dependence is of complicated nature, and its computation a difficult task, in aqueous electrolyte solutions [21], all these difficulties are enhanced when we have more complicated systems, as those described in this paper. An *a* dependence on the electrolyte concentration, in a system containing an ion (K^+) which produces a break-effect on the water structure, inside a very hydrophilic media (gel I), may justify the poor correlation between the experimental data and the eq. (6).

This dependence decreases with more charge density ions, Li^+, and more cross-linked polymers [20 (pp. 96)]. Once the size of the hydrated LiCl species is larger than the KCl species, it seems reliable that an increase in the cross-linker concentration makes difficult the diffusivity of such species. As a consequence the diffusing entities will tend to diffuse decreasing the mean distance of approach of the ions and therefore the dependence of *a* on concentration becomes more relevant.

Table 6. Regression results of application of Free Volume Model, eq. (6), to electrolyte diffusion in hydrogels with different percentage of cross-linking.

Gel	electrolyte	r_s* / Å	ln (k_1)	k_2	R^2
I	KCl	3.8	4.8	1.8	0.99
II	KCl	3.8	12	0.62	0.97
I	LiCl	4.25	2.2	0.79	0.96
II	LiCl	4.25	12	0.50	0.94

* The values of r_s are the values of the minimum mean distance of approach of the ions [29].

The k_2 values show also that the diffusion of KCl is more dependent on the water concentration than the LiCl. This should be expected, if we take into account the structure-breaking effect of the K^+ ions (and also Cl^-) on the water structure. Therefore, the polymer-solvent interactions, or even the possible ion-polymer interactions, are more important in the KCl systems, and decrease with the increase of cross-linker. As a consequence we may point out that the electrolyte diffusion is not dependent on the macromolecular structure itself but on the hydrated macromolecular structure.

The diffusion coefficients of KCl and LiCl in MMA-AAm hydrogels do not change with the polymer volume fraction. As a consequence, the increase of D_F with the increase of electrolyte concentration should have another explanation, on basis of eq. (7). Figure 3 shows how the factor (k_c r_s) changes with the KCl and LiCl concentration inside matrices. These figures show the decrease of (k_c r_s) with an increase of C, and this should be due to r_s decrease because k_c is a constant for each gel/electrolyte system. Such a decrease can be interpreted as a close position of the ions with consequent ion-pair formation. This form of electrolyte is characterised by less resistance to motion through the liquid than it would be in the case of two separate ions. Consequently, ion-pairs make a contribution to an electrolyte flux increasing the apparent diffusion coefficient D_F. Such an assumption is in agreement with experimental results reported by Zaikov [20 (pp.101-102)].

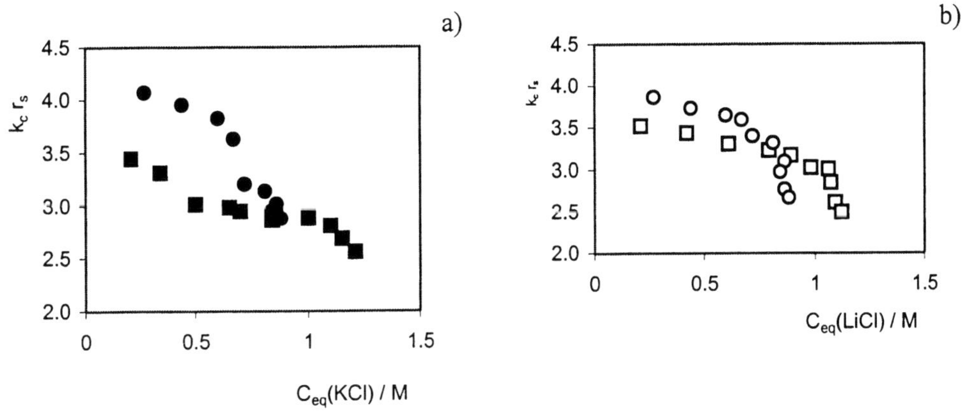

Figure 3. Dependence of k_c r_s on the concentration of the KCl (black points) and LiCl (white points) aqueous solution in the gel III (a) and in the gel IV (b).

More significant variation of r_s with concentration, which is observed for gel IV, is a consequence of the decrease of the water content available as diffusing media. The later results in an easier approach of the counter-ions to each other.

The values of k_c, can be estimated for all systems using eq. (7) and data reported in Figure 3 if we extrapolate the fitting lines to C = 0. If concentration is very low (close to infinitesimal values), the ions diffuse as single entities and their radius, r, can be calculated directly from the Stokes-Einstein equation

$$r = (k_B T) / (6 \pi \eta D^0) \qquad (9)$$

where k_B is the Boltzmann's constant, T is the temperature and η is the water viscosity at that temperature (T = 298 K in our case). The Nernst limiting diffusion coefficients, D^0, of KCl and LiCl were calculated from the limiting ionic conductivities [13] and are 1.994×10^{-9} m^2 s^{-1} and 1.367×10^{-9} m^2 s^{-1}, respectively. Introducing experimental data into eq. (9) we find the radii of KCl and LiCl as 1.229 Å and 1.793 Å, respectively.

The calculated values of k_c are reported in Table 7 showing: a) the different effect of KCl and LiCl on the polymer-water interactions (this is in close agreement with the possible effect of the ions on the water molecule structure); b) that the values of k_c obtained using the radius of the electrolyte (r_s) are three, two times higher than those reported by Amsden [25] for polyacrylamide systems. This means that when we are talking about strong electrolytes we must take into account the mean distance of approach instead of the solute radius, which is meaningless in this case. Substituting the solute radius computed using equation (8), by the mean distance of approach of the ions, *a*, in dilute solutions (3.63 Å and 4.32 Å [13] for KCl and LiCl respectively), we find the values of k_c (Table 7) which agree with those reported in literature [25].

Table 7. Estimated values of k_c for the polyacrylamide/electrolyte/water systems, using the radius of the electrolyte (r) and the mean distance of approach of the ions (*a*) from [13].

	r / Å	*a* / Å	$r_s k_c$ (C_{eq}=0)	k_c (r_s=r)	k_c (r_s=*a*)
Gel I / KCl	1.229	3.63	3.79	3.1	1.0
Gel II / KCl			4.22	3.4	1.2
Gel I / LiCl	1.793	4.32	3.64	2.0	0.84
Gel II / LiCl			4.04	2.2	0.93

The analysis of k_c values shows that: i) the dependence of D_F on the "solute radius" is less affected by the polymer-water interactions in the systems containing LiCl; ii) as water concentration decreases inside the matrix the probability of ion-pairs formation increases, and, consequently, the diffusion coefficients are more variable within a small range of concentration.

The association of the electrolytes at higher c concentrations is comproved by the fact that there is a linear relationship between D_F as a function of C to both electrolytes. In the case of KCl-systems, and considering the experimental D_F to concentrations higher than 0.7 and 0.6 M, to gel III and IV respectively, we found a linear relationship that crosses the origin. This clear shows that the diffusion coefficient is concentration square (C^2) dependent, which is due to the equilibrium between the ions and the associated ion-pair [31]. In the case of the LiCl-systems the variation of D_F with C, although linear to the highest c(LiCl) concentrations show a high slope suggesting that the diffusion process can be affected by other processes than the ion-pairs formation.

CONCLUSIONS

The diffusion of strong electrolytes in polyacrylamides with different degrees of cross-linking is driven by two main factors: the water volume fraction and the hydration features of the cations. In this case, the diffusion process can be explained taking into account the ion-ion, ion-water, and water-polymer interactions. The free volume model gives the mathematical tool to interpret such data.

With an introduction of a hydrophobic co-monomer, the methyl methacrylate, the diffusion coefficients of KCl and LiCl in co-polymers depend on a wider set of interactions, where the most relevant one is clearly the ion-ion interactions. An application of Cukier's model [26] made possible to find that the increase of the diffusion coefficients is due to a decrease in the mean distance of approach of the ions. This can lead to the formation of ion-pairs and their contribution to the total flux of an electrolyte. An increase of methyl methacrylate content in the polymer chain results in stronger dependence of effective diffusion coefficient of an electrolyte on the apparent radius of the solute.

The synthesised neutral gels show selective transport properties to KCl and LiCl aqueous solutions. Whereas the alteration of the cross-linker concentration only enhances such properties, the synthesis of MMA-AAm hydrogels clearly induce ion-pair formation of these electrolytes in a concentration range where, in free solutions, ion-pairs do not exist.

ACKNOWLEDGMENT:

Financial support from POCTI/QUI/39593/2001 and POCTI/35415/QUI /2000 is gratefully acknowledged.

REFERENCES

1. T. Tanaka, *Encyl. Polym. Sci. Eng.*, V.6, 514 (1986).
2. K.S. Kazanskii, S.A. Dubrovskii, *Adv. Polym. Sci.*, V.97, 104 (1992).
3. W.-F. Lee, R.-J. Wu, *J. Appl. Polym. Sci.*, V.62, 1099 (1996).
4. R.C. Allen, H.R. Maurer, Eds. *Electrophoresis and Isoelectric Focusing in Polyacrylamides Gels* (de Gruyter: Berlin, 1974).
5. A.Ya. Polishchuk, G. E. Zaikov, *Multicomponent Transport in Polymer Systems for Controlled Release* (Gordon and Breach Sci. Publ, New York, 1997).
6. J.P. Baker, L.H. Hong, H.W. Blanch, J.M. Prausnitz, *Macromolecules*, V.27, 1446 (1994).
7. C. Duval, *Inorganic Thermogravimetric Aanalysis* (Elsevier, New York, 1953).
8. H. Tobita, A.E. Hamielec, *Polymer*, V.31, 1546 (1991).
9. J.A. Wiersma, M. Bos, A.J. Pennings, *Polym. Bull.*, V.33, 615 (1994).
10. A.J.M. Valente, A.Ya. Polishchuk, V.M.M. Lobo, H. Burrows, *Langmuir*, V.16, 6475 (2000).
11. A.Ya. Polishchuk, A.J.M. Valente, G. Camino, M.P. Luda, N.N. Madyuskin, V.M.M. Lobo, G.E. Zaikov, M. Revellino, *J. Appl. Polym. Sci.*, V.83, 1157 (2002).
12. O.Ya. Samoilov, *Discuss. Faraday Soc.*, V.24, 141 (1957).
13. R.A. Robinson and R.H. Stokes, *Electrolyte Solutions* (Butterworths, London, 1959), 2nd ed.
14. M. Ilavski, J. Hrouz, J. Stegskal, K. Bouchal, *Macromolecules*, V.17, 2868 (1984).
15. P.H. Corkhill, A.M. Jolly, C.O. Ng, B. J. Tighe, *Polymer*, V.28, 1758 (1987).
16. H.S. Frank, F. Frank, *J. Chem. Phys.*, V.48, 4746 (1968).
17. V.M.M. Lobo, A.J.M. Valente, A.Ya. Polishchuk, G. Geuskens, *J. Mol. Liquids*, V.94, 179 (2001).
18. A.J.M. Valente, A.Ya. Polishchuk, V.M.M. Lobo, G. Geuskens, *Eur. Polym. J.*, V.94, 179 (2002).
19. V.M.M. Lobo, A.J.M. Valente, Port. Electrochim. Acta, V.14, 133 (1996); A.J.M. Valente, V.M.M. Lobo, *Port. Electrochim.* Acta, V.18, 159 (2000).
20. G. E. Zaikov, A. L. Iordanskii and V. S. Markin, *Diffusion of Electrolytes in Polymers* (VSP, Utrecht, 1988).
21. L. De Mayer, G. Kessling, *J. Mol. Liquids*, V.67, 193 (1995).
22. A. M. Muhr, J. M. V. Blanshard, *Polymer*, V.23, 1012 (1982).
23. A.Ya. Polishchuk, L.A. Zimina, N.N. Madyuskin, G.E. Zaikov, *Polym. Sci.*, V.35, 80 (1993).
24. A.Ya. Polishchuk, G.E. Zaikov, J.H. Petropoulos, *Int. J. Polymeric Mater.*, V.25, 1 (1994).
25. B. Amsden, *Macromolecules*, V.31, 8382 (1998).

26. R.I. Cukier, *Macromolecules*, V.17, 252 (1984).
27. V.M.M. Lobo, *Handbook of Electrolyte Solutions*. (Elsevier, Amsterdam, 1990).
28. H.J. Naghash and O. Okay, *J. Appl. Polym. Sci.*, V.60, 971 (1996).
29. V.M.M.Lobo, A.C.F. Ribeiro, S.G.C.S. Andrade, *Ber. Buns. Phys. Chem.*, V.99, 713 (1995).
30. J. Kielland, *J. Am. Chem. Soc.*, V.59, 1675 (1973).
31. E.L. Cussler, *Diffusion, Mass Transfer in Fluid Systems* (Cambridge, Cambridge Univ. Press, 2000), 2nd ed.

Chapter 2

DIFFERENTIAL MUTUAL DIFFUSION COEFFICIENTS OF ELECTROLYTES MEASURED BY AN OPEN-ENDED CONDUCTIMETRIC CAPILLARY CELL: A REVIEW

Victor M.M. Lobo, Artur J.M. Valente and Ana C.F. Ribeiro
Department of Chemistry, University of Coimbra, 3004-535 Coimbra, Portugal.
vlobo@ci.uc.pt, avalente@ci.uc.pt, anacfrib@ci.uc.pt.

ABSTRACT

An open-ended capillary cell was developed to measure accurate mutual differential diffusion coefficients. We discuss the conditions that make this technique reliable. Experimental diffusion coefficients of different electrolytes in aqueous solution measured by this technique will be shown in a schematic way. These experimental data will be discussed in terms of Onsager-Fuoss and Pikal theories.

Key Words: Diffusion; Diffusion Coefficients; Aqueous Solutions; Electrolytes; Ionic Solutes

INTRODUCTION

The study of diffusion processes in electrolyte solutions is important for both fundamental (for a deep understanding of aqueous electrolyte structure) and practical (data for industrial and medical purposes, environment, and a variety of sciences from geology to corrosion) interests. However, whereas self-diffusion coefficients on electrolyte solutions may be obtained from electroanalytical methods using experimental techniques of relatively easy execution, the mutual differential diffusion coefficients, D, in those solutions presents difficult experimental problems. In fact, techniques developed still in the XIX and early XX century produced so unreliable results that the famous International Critical Tables showed discrepancies of more than 100%! Sir B. Clark [1] devoted much of his scientific efforts in the first half of the XX century trying to obtain precise and accurate diffusion coefficients of electrolyte solutions of simple salts, using an optical method based on the variation of the refractive index due to a concentration gradient caused by diffusion. Optical methods based on this principal were also developed by a number of experimentalists [2] based on the Gouy interference phenomenon [3]. Also, optical methods are unsuitable for dilute solutions because then the variations of refractive index are so small that cannot be measured. In the second half of the XX century, a conductimetric method was developed by Harned [4-5]. The cell was highly successful in the sense that it managed to measure D with an imprecision smaller than 1% (around 0.5%) and believed to be very accurate because the results for very dilute solutions (around 0.01 M) of 1:1 salts were in agreement with Onsager-Fuoss theory. However, it also presented tremendous experimental difficulties: to measure, say, D of KCl 0.1 M, it would take a week and the number of unsuccessful runs was so high that each of the many Ph.D. students would measure only a few concentrations [6-23]. R.H. Stokes [24] developed a diaphragm cell, which we also have used, but it gives only integral diffusion coefficients, not differential, is a relative method (needs calibration), and is only good for relatively high concentrations because of the surface effects on the sintered glass.

The success of the open ended capillary technique, developed for self-diffusion coefficients and using radioisotopes, and conductimetry as a method of following minute concentrations differences, as shown in Harned's cell, led to the development of an open ended capillary cell where concentration variations are followed conductimetrically. The system seems to be highly successful (see Tables 1-5) and has been prized [25]. In fact, the idea of having symmetry in the positioning of the capillaries and electrode buffers any minute temperature alterations. So, the temperature is constant within ± 0.001 °C as tested with an accurate digital thermometer with a resolution of 0.001 °C. This may be due to the fact that the solution is inside a glass tank, itself in a good thermostat (uncertainty ≤ 0.01 °C).

Also, resistance readings in steady isoconcentrational conditions show a stability up to the last digit of a 5 figure reading for hours, that is, it proves that those resistance readings in a normal experiment are due to a concentration variation, not temperature effects.

A considerable instrumentation development in the techniques of measuring refractive index variations in a thin capillary due to the widespread commercial interest in chromatographic techniques has allowed a significant development of the Taylor dispersion technique to measure D.

Unfortunately, there frequently is a confusion concerning mutual and self-diffusion coefficients, and so the concepts related to self-diffusion (*intradiffusion*, *tracer diffusion*, *single ion diffusion*, *ionic diffusion*, *translational diffusion*) and distinction between *self-diffusion* and *mutual diffusion* (*interdiffusion*, *concentration diffusion*, *salt diffusion*, *chemical diffusion*, *collective diffusion*), will now be analysed.

In fact, it is very common to find misunderstandings concerning the meaning of a parameter, frequently just denoted by D and merely called diffusion coefficient, in the scientific literature, communications, meetings, or simple discussions among researchers. Actually, many papers reporting data on diffusion coefficients do not specify if they report to self or mutual diffusion and frequently it is not clear from reading the paper, or hearing the communication, that the authors are aware of the difference or, in some cases, they are convinced that they are mutual diffusion when actually they are not, or vice-versa.

It is therefore convenient to have in mind the following terms:

(1) Diffusion in a pure liquid, such as the diffusion of water in water. The term *self-diffusion* has always been used for this case.
(2) Diffusion in binary or multicomponent electrolyte solutions where the labelled species is isotopic with one of the components. [e.g. $^{22}Na^{+}$ in aqueous NaCl]. For this process the term *tracer-diffusion* arose naturally from the use of trace species which were labelled by their radioactivity. *Trace ion*, *single ion*, *ionic* or *translational* diffusion coefficients are alternative names. In 1965, Albright and Mills [26] coined the term *intradiffusion* for this process and defined it as the mutual diffusion between two chemically equivalent components. The chemical equivalence of the isotopic species is the important feature and allows expressions to be developed between the diffusion coefficients of binary and ternary systems. In intradiffusion, also, the labelled component does not have to be present in trace amounts as is essential in case (3) below.
(3) Diffusion in multicomponent electrolyte solutions where the diffusing labelled species is not isotopic with another component. [e.g. $^{22}Na^{+}$ in aqueous KCl]. The labelled species is necessarily in trace amounts and the term *tracer-diffusion* can be applied to this process.

We normally use only the term *self-diffusion* because, firstly, it is useful to have a covering term for both intradiffusion and tracer-diffusion and, secondly, it is in general usage by electrochemists who are not specialists in the field of diffusion. A further justification for the use of *self-diffusion* as an umbrella term is that all of the diffusion processes detailed above are described by an autocorrelation function [27].

A variety of symbols have been ued for *self-diffusion* coefficients: among them $\mathbf{D_i^*}$, $\mathbf{D_i}$, $\mathbf{D_i^s}$ and **D(i)**. The form **D(i)** is preferable in order to avoid awkward subscripts.

It should be made clear that the self-diffusion process is fundamentally different from that of the diffusion of electrolytes as a whole (termed mutual, inter-, or concentration diffusion, or even salt diffusion, chemical diffusion or collective diffusion). If there is a salt concentration gradient in a binary electrolyte solution, then the constraint of maintaining electrical neutrality ensures that positive and negative ions move from the region of higher to lower concentration at the same speed. On a volume-fixed and most other reference frames, there is only one mutual or interdiffusion coefficient in this system. In self-diffusion on the other hand, the electrical neutrality restraint does not apply and the three species (ions and solvent) have independent diffusion coefficients. The same considerations apply to self-diffusion in multicomponent solutions. It should be noted also that self-diffusion coefficients essentially do not depend on the frame of reference. Further, since the activity coefficient on the trace species does not change in a virtually uniform solution, the thermodynamic factor, $d\ln a_i/d\ln x_i$ (a is the activity and x is the mole fraction of component i) which appears in the equations describing mutual diffusion, becomes unity.

There is no simple relation between mutual and self-diffusion coefficients except when the solute is at infinitesimal concentration. In this case a variant of the Nernst Equation can be written in its simplest form for 1:1 electrolytes as

$$\mathbf{D_m}^0 = 2\,(\mathbf{D_a}^0.\mathbf{D_c}^0)/(\mathbf{D_a}^0 + \mathbf{D_c}^0)$$

where $\mathbf{D}_m^0$ is the limiting mutual diffusion coefficient of the salt and $\mathbf{D}_a^0$ and $\mathbf{D}_c^0$ are the limiting self-diffusion coefficients of anion and cation, respectively.

Because of the phonetic similarity between the words *intradiffusion* and *interdiffusion*, and the not so obvious difference to some people between the prefixes *inter-* and *intra-*, the term *mutual diffusion* is preferable. It is also better than *concentration diffusion, salt diffusion, chemical diffusion or collective diffusion*.

THE OPEN-ENDED CONDUCTIMETRIC CAPILLARY CELL

Measurements of conductance provide a sensitive and accurate method of following concentration changes in solutions of simple electrolytes; they are well suited to the study of small differences of concentration in dilute solutions, and can be profitably used in the study of diffusion. This fact was exploited by Harned *et al.* [5-7, 28-29] whose work on the diffusion of dilute aqueous electrolytes remains pre-eminent. In brief words, Harned's cell consists of a sheared boundary cell in which restricted diffusion is allowed to occur between two dilute electrolyte solutions, or between a dilute electrolyte solution and the pure solvent. The more concentrated solution was placed in the lower half of the cell, a sheared boundary formed, and diffusion allowed to occur until the transition from free to restricted diffusion had taken place. Concentration changes were followed by measuring the conductivity at two planes symmetrically disposed with respect to the centre of the cell. This restricted diffusion cell, described in great detail in [30 (p.124)], allows to measure genuine differential diffusion coefficients at the mean concentration of the experiment. This mean is measured at the end of the diffusion run by allowing the contents of the cell to become homogeneously mixed and then measuring the conductivity. The experimental technique requires great care since the diffusion column, stabilized only by gravity, could easily be disturbed by thermal convection or mechanical vibration. The problems involved may be judged from the fact that in order to mix the cell contents at the end of the experiment, it was only necessary to place a lamp near the enclosure in which the diffusion cell is housed. The method is applicable at concentrations down to 1×10^{-3} M.

An alternative conductimetric technique was developed by Lobo to measure mutual differential diffusion coefficients in solutions of electrolytes with simplicity and high precision. The measurement of D is done avoiding some of the experimental problems associated with Harned-type cells by allowing the diffusion process to occur inside open-ended capillaries [31-32]. This cell is operationally much simpler than any of the other available systems and has successfully been used with solutions more diluted than possible with Harned's cell and also with reasonably concentrated solutions. Although a substantial amount of work has been published using this cell, a description of the diffusion cell is not easily available. For this reason, the open ended conductimetric capillary cell will be described in great detail in the following sections.

The Design

Two precision bore capillaries of equal length and internal diameters (2.5 mm) were each sealed at one end by a platinum electrode and placed vertically above each other, the open tip of the upper capillary facing downwards and that of the lower one facing upwards, with their vertical axis coincident. The open ends are separated by about 20 mm and the whole system is immersed in an electrolyte solution of concentration c_b. A third, central, electrode is placed at a point equidistant from the open ends of the capillaries and displaced from their common axis. The diffusion capillaries are sealed to other two supporting tubes (see Figure 1 for cell description) and the cell is immersed in a rectangular tank filled with electrolyte solution of concentration c_b.

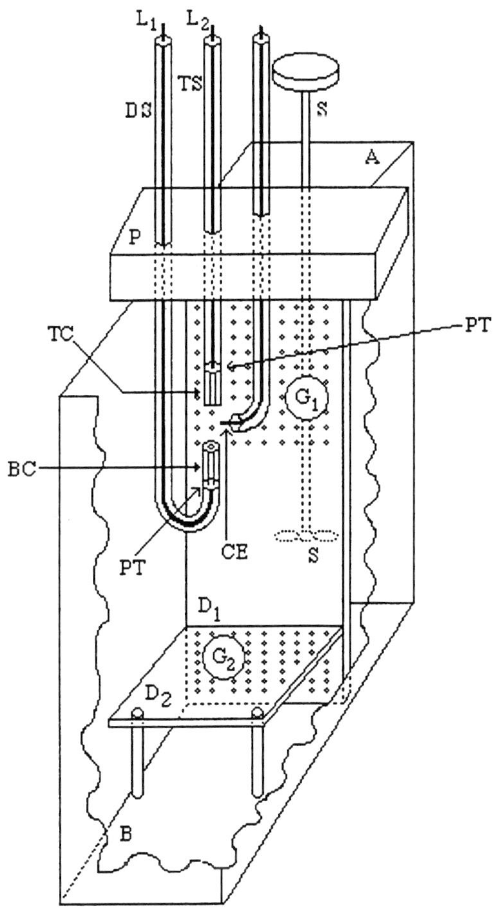

Figure 1. Schematic representation of the open-ended capillary cell. TS,BS: support capillaries; TC, BC: top and bottom diffusion capillaries; CE: central electrode; PT: platinum electrodes; D_1, D_2: perspex sheets; S: glass stirrer; P: Perspex block; G_1, G_2: perforations in Perspex sheets; A, B: sections of the tank; L_1, L_2:small diameter coaxial leads.

The tank is divided internally by a "chair", which consists in two “Perspex” sheets that will produce a streamlined flow between the two open-ended diffusion capillaries as a consequence of appropriate perforations.

The upper capillary is filled with a solution of concentration ($0.75c_b$), the lower one with a solution of concentration ($1.25c_b$), and the electrical resistance ratio (W_t=R’/R’’) between the central electrode and the upper (R’) and the lower (R’’) electrodes in the capillaries is measured as a function of time. Here and elsewhere, ’ and ’’ denote upper and lower capillaries, respectively. The information required to evaluate D can be extracted from the above W_t=R'/R'' ratio.

The Method Theory

The diffusion process in the open-ended conductimetric capillary cell can be described using the Fick's 2nd law equation

$$\partial c/\partial t = D\,(\partial^2 c/\partial x^2) \tag{1}$$

Using the appropriate initial and boundary conditions of the technique

$$t = 0: \qquad c_t = c_0\ (0 < x < a),\ c_t = c_b\ (x > a) \tag{2}$$

$$t > 0: \qquad c_t = c_b\ (x > a),\ (dc/dx)_{x=0} = 0 \tag{3}$$

where a is the capillary length and x = 0 at the ended end of the capillary. c_0 is the initial concentration of the electrolyte inside the capillary. Using eqs. (2) and (3) a solution of eq. (1) can be found [33], and describes the evolution of the electrolyte concentration, c_t, at a x point as a function of time, t, according to

$$c_t = \sum B_n \exp[-\pi^2\,(2n+1)^2\,D\,t/(4\,a^2)]\,\cos\,[\pi\,(2n+1)\,x\,/(2\,a)] + c_b \tag{4}$$

where

$$B_n = (-1)^n\,[4\,(c_0 - c_b)]\,/\,[\pi\,(2n+1)] \tag{5}$$

At long times, say t > 1000 minutes, only the first term of the serie (eq. 4) is significant. As a consequence eq. (4) can be simplified in the form of [32, 34]

$$q = q_0\,(8/\pi^2)\,\exp\,(-\lambda\,t) + \text{neglected terms} \tag{6}$$

where q and q_0 are functions which relate concentration with time t and t=0, respectively. λ can be defined as

$$\lambda = (\pi^2\,D)\,/\,(4\,a^2) \tag{7}$$

On the other hand, the electrical resistance, R, between the central and the top (or bottom) electrode can be defined as a sum of two different terms

$$R = r + R_t = r + (a\,/\,A)\int_{\xi=0}^{1} \rho\,d\xi \tag{8}$$

where r is the electrical resistance (independent of time) from the open end capillary cell to the central electrode, and R_t represents the resistance of the solution in a capillary at time t. ρ is the specific electrical resistance the capillary, A is the cross-section of the capillary tube, and $\xi = x/a$.

The measured resistance ratio is

$$W_t = (R'_t + r') / (R''_t + r'') \quad (9)$$

and we may derive from it the quantity Y_t defined by

$$Y_t = (W_t - 1) / (W_t + 1) \quad (10)$$

If both tubes are initially filled with c_b solution, we achieve the same situation as would occur after infinite time in a diffusion experiment starting with a finite concentration difference. For this case we have

$$Y_\infty = (W_\infty - 1) / (W_\infty + 1) \quad (11)$$

Ideally W_∞ should be unity and Y_∞ should be zero. In practice owing to slight imperfections in gluing the platinum electrodes to the closed end of the glass capillaries, to negligible differences in the lengths of the capillaries, and to asymmetry in the position of the centre tap and in its environment, and also due to possible imperfections in the bridge, Y_∞ is normally not exactly zero though very close to it. A typical value is 5×10^{-4} [31]. It can, however, be shown that $(Y_t - Y_\infty)$ is a good measure of the progress of diffusion at long times.

If now we consider a function h defined as

$$h = (c - c_b)/ c_b \quad (12)$$

the specific resistance may be expanded as a power series in h in the form

$$\rho = \rho_b \sum b_m h^m \quad (13)$$

where ρ_b corresponds to concentration c_b at h=0. However as D is computed from readings at high values of time t, eq. (13) can be simplified:

$$\rho = \rho_b (1 + b h) \quad (14)$$

From eq. (8) and (14), R can be written as

$$R = r + (a\, \rho_b / A) + (a\, \rho_b / A) \int_{\xi=0}^{1} bh \, d\xi = r + R_\infty (1 + q) \quad (15)$$

where R_∞ ($= a\,\rho_b / A$) is the electrical resistance inside the capillary when $c_t = c_b$, and $q = \int_{\xi=0}^{1} bh \, d\xi$.

As a consequence, the expression for Y_t becomes

$$Y_t = [(r' + R'_\infty) - (r'' + R''_\infty) + (R'_\infty q' - R''_\infty q'')] / R^T \tag{16}$$

where R represents the total resistance between the electrodes PT (Fig. 1). Since R'_∞ is very nearly equal to R''_∞, the relatively small term ($R'_\infty q' - R''_\infty q''$) can be written $R_{\infty,av}$ ($q'-q''$). The method of filling the diffusion cell ensures that h' = -h'' initially, and since the capillaries are of equal lengths and the diffusion coefficients in the two capillaries are effectively the same, we may expect that h' = -h'' at all times. At the same time for direct measurements we may conclude that $R^T = R^T_\infty$ at all times.

Thus we can write with a sufficient approximation that

$$Y_t = Y_\infty + (R_{\infty,av} / R^T_\infty)\,(q' - q'') \tag{17}$$

with

$$(q' - q'') = b \int_{\xi=0}^{1} (h' - h'')\, d\xi \tag{18}$$

From eq. (6) we have

$$\int_{\xi=0}^{1} h'\, d\xi = - \int_{\xi=0}^{1} h''\, d\xi = q_0\, (8/\pi^2) \exp(-\lambda\, t) \tag{19}$$

We thus finally obtain, using eqs. (17), (18) and (19)

$$(Y_t - Y_\infty) = [(R_{\infty,av} / R^T_\infty)\,(16/\pi^2)\, q_0\, b] \exp(-\lambda\, t) \tag{20}$$

or

$$\ln (Y_t - Y_\infty) = \text{constant} - \lambda\, t \tag{21}$$

Therefore, plotting the experimental results $\ln(Y_t - Y_\infty)$ as a function of time, and using a specifically designed computer program of successively interactions coupled with the minimum square deviations method, a straight line equation is obtained, and the corresponding slope is directly proportional to the diffusion coefficient by using eq. (7).

Description of the Different Cell Components

The diffusion capillary tubes are glass made and have a length around 2.0-2.5 cm. The capillary length is very accurately measured with a micrometer with 0.001 mm resolution, once an error of, say, 2 % in the value of *a* (eq. 7), would produce an error of 4 % in the computed diffusion coefficient.

The diffusion capillaries are positioned 10 mm from each other, with the central tap in an equidistant position from the open-ends of these two capillaries, in the same axis. However, a displacement of the diffusion tubes of about 1 cm, using as reference a vertical axis which passes at the middle of a diffusion tube, can be neglected, once the diffusion process does not suffer any significant alteration (less than 0.4 %).

The internal and external diameters were 2.5 mm and 8 mm, respectively. With such dimensions we may neglect all the error sources provoked by mechanical vibrations on the mass transport.

The platinum electrode discs (6 mm diameter and 0.05 mm thickness) are cemented to one end of each capillary tubes with a cianoacrylic glue. This kind of glues offers a quick gluing time, commercial availability, and physical and chemical resistance to metal/glass contact. The cementation of the platinum electrode is also very important once any glue should diffuse to the internal diameter (equal to the internal diameter of the diffusion capillary tubes). If so, an increase of electrical resistance of the circuit is observed, and the electrical resistance ratio measurement is not anymore possible. The platinum discs must be absent of any oxides, impurities, oils, etc.

The diffusion tubes are attached by PVC and glue to the supporting tubes (with the platinum discs at middle), which are mounted on a "Perspex" block P (Fig. 1) 20×145×45 mm with the help of nylon screws. The use of PVC also contributes to a decrease of electrical capacitances and noise of the whole electrical circuit.

The electrical leads contact with the platinum discs through a drop of mercury. After setting up the whole cell, its operationality could be tested using a voltmeter.

Another test to check the operationality of the cell can be made by measuring the experimental parameter TR_∞. In the previous sections we have mentioned that measuring the W_t monitorises the diffusion process. However, due to experimental and simplicity reasons, the experimental parameter which is indeed measured is TR, which is related with W_t according to

$$TR = 10^4 / (1 + W_t) \qquad (22)$$

When the diffusion tubes are filled with the same solution of concentration c_b, then $TR=TR_\infty$ and a close value of 5000 should be measured. Therefore the analysis of TR is an accurate way to check the reproducibility as well as the good conditions of the cell. Even so changes in more or less 20 units in TR_∞ do not influence the accurate value of D. This parameter (TR_∞ or W_∞) is indeed very important not only because gives information about the status of the cell as well as it is necessary to calculate D. Once it corresponds at equilibrium or pseudo-equilibrium conditions, many other factors may influence it, as for example, temperature, vibrations, etc.

In order to avoid lack of isothermal conditions during the experiments (an increase of 5 °C will correspond to an increase in D of about 12.7 %), the conductimetric cell is positioned in a tank (B in Figure 1), which is immersed in a thermostatic bath (with a thermostat resolution of 0.01 °C; this resolution will contribute to maintain D inside the experimental error). It is also important to point out that the temperature changes caused by electrical current, in this cell, can be neglected; in fact considering a capillary tube 24 mm length, and with 8.5 mm and 2.5 mm of external and internal diameters, respectively, and taking as example studies with KCl 0.1 M, the temperature changes occurring due to the electrical current is 10.1×10^{-5} K.

The tank containing the electrolyte bulk solution is a glass tank 20x14x6 cm and the two larger walls are only 4 mm thick, to facilitate thermal equilibration.

Techniques

Diffusion is followed by measuring of the ratio of electrical resistances of the electrolyte in both capillaries, as time proceeds, and by continuously measuring of the impedance ratios. In one of the techniques we use an alternating current transformer bridge and an oscilloscope where an ellipse is manually reduced to a horizontal line. In this system it is possible to measure the pure ohmic resistance, by manually balancing the capacity effects, and therefore go to concentration of 0.001 M. The appropriate frequency is 4000 Hz. In another technique (automatic system) used for lower concentrations, that is, for resistances of the order of tens of thousands or hundreds of thousands of ohms (solutions of the order of 0.01 M or 0.001 M) does not give reliable values if we work with frequencies 4000 Hz. The possible cause is due to the fact we measure impedances ratios and so we have effects capacities not eliminated. We overcame this difficulty by using frequencies lower than the 4000 Hz previously taken as the most appropriate [35].

Δl Effect

Using capillary tubes was possible to design an elegant composition whereby a streamlined flow of solution across the mouth of the capillaries effectively eliminates the Δl-effect [36] once the diffusion path is very nearly equal to the physical length of the tubes. This way, experimental difficulties faced by other techniques [37-39] can be overcoming.

The so-called "Δl effect", which are closest associated with the use of capillaries, can be caused by two different factors: a) If the solution stirring is too rapid or turbulent, part of the active solution may be swept more or less continuously out of the capillary during the diffusion run. In these circumstances, the diffusion path of the diffusing particles is lower than the real diffusion capillary tube length [40], and the diffusion decreases in order to favour the mass flux by convection; b) If there is not enough stirring or even if it doesn't exist at all, an opposite effect will occur. In fact, in these conditions the diffusion path of the solution is higher than the capillary length. For example, the "diffusion coefficients" of KCl 0.01 M, without solution stirring, at 20 °C and at 25 °C are, 1.0 and 0.5 % lower, than the D obtained by Harned, at the same temperatures, respectively [7, 29].

Using the open-ended conductimetric capillary cell, the diffusion coefficient of KCl solutions does not change within an interval of stirrer velocity between 70 and 100 rpm. However changing the stirrer velocity to 200 rpm, an increase in D is observed. This shows that at, e.g., 72 rpm (the stirrer velocity used in almost all experiments), the diffusion path and the diffusion capillary length are the same, and the Δl effect can be neglected. This conclusion is also valid for other electrolyte solutions [41].

Streamlined Flow

As previously described the mass transport of the diffusing species occurs by diffusion in a streamlined flow. This is a direct consequence of the cell's design. The tank is divided in two sections by a "Perspex" sheet (D_1 and D_2, Fig. 1). To provide this flow there is in section A of the glass tank, Fig. 1, a stirrer, S (made of glass and with three blades of approximately oval shape 2 cm long and 1.3 cm of maximum width), rotating at 72 rpm when fed a 60 c/s signal at 200-220 V. The stirrer propels the solution downwards, and forces it to pass to section B through a sort of grating G_2. This grating is made by drilling holes 1 mm in diameter and 5 mm apart from each other in a Perspex sheet. The solution then flows to compartment A through similar grating, G_1, in the upper part of the tank. The turbulent flux generated by the stirring will dissipate their turbulent kinetic energy, passing to streamlined regime after crossing the holes of grating G_2. Using the fluid mechanical principles it is possible to estimate the necessary time to pass from turbulent to streamlined flux.

Using the stirrer frequency (60 c s^{-1}) and the length of each blade of 20 mm, the velocity of the stirrer is approximately 0.15 m s^{-1}. The turbulent kinetic energy (E_c) is given by

$$E_c = (3/2)\, u^2 \quad (23)$$

where u is the velocity of the turbulent particles.

The dissipation rate of the turbulent kinetic energy, ε, is obtained through

$$\varepsilon = u^3 / l \quad (24)$$

where l is the diameter of the holes (G_1 and G_2) existing in the Perspex sheets.

From equations (23) and (24), the dependence of E_c on time, t, can be described as

$$dE_c/dt = -\,\varepsilon \quad (25)$$

and turbulent kinetic energy as a function of t can be written as

$$E_c = (3/2)\,(9\, l^2\, u_0^2) / (t_1\, u_0 + 3\, l)^2 \quad (26)$$

where the subscripts 0 and 1 indicate the initial instant when the vortex acquires its own inertia and the time when such vortex dissipates in the bulk passing to a streamlined flux. For the sake of simplicity we assume the velocities of the vortex turbulent particles and stirrer as the same.

When the kinetic energy of the vortex, in the Kolmogorov's scale, E_{cK} (eq. 27), is lower than a critical (limit) value, it is possible to calculate the interval of time necessary to pass from turbulent to streamlined flow

$$E_{cK} = (3 / 2)\, v_K^2 \qquad (27)$$

where v_K is the velocity of the particles, in the Kolmogorov's scale, obtained using

$$v_K = (\nu\, \varepsilon)^{1/4} \quad (28)$$

where ν is the kinematic viscosity of the flow.

Let's take as example an aqueous solution of potassium thiocyanate 0.02 M, at 25 °C. The kinematic viscosity of this solution is 1.7×10^{-5} m^2 s^{-1} [42]. The v_k is equal to 0.087 m s^{-1} and the corresponding kinetic energy is equal to $1.13\text{x}10^{-2}$ m^2 s^{-1} per mass unity. Substituting these values in eq. (26) at time t_l=0.01 s is obtained. After this time the viscose forces become predominant on the turbulent particles of the flow, which have cross the "Perspex" sheet holes (G_2) at t=0, and a streamlined flow appears. Assuming now the vortex velocity as the same than the stirrer rate (0.15 m s^{-1}), the distance necessary to go through until reaching the streamlined flux is about 1.5 mm. This distance is reached under the "Perspex" sheet and ensures that in part A of the cell, as well as between the two diffusion capillaries, a streamlined flux occurs. For this reason, the measurement of an one-dimensional flux in an isothermal media is ensured. The streamlined flow, with these experimental conditions can be macroscopically observed using few drops of a mixture of oil and carbon tetrachloride (in proportions that a density equal than the water can be obtained).

A Typical Run

A standard procedure to check the cell is to use KCl solution 0.1 M. This example is also valid as a typical run for any electrolyte and concentration. A "top" solution of concentration 0.075 M and a "bottom" solution of concentration 0.125 M are prepared, each in a 2 L volumetric flask. The bulk solution of concentration c_b = 0.1 M is prepared by mixing 1 L of the top solution with 1 L of the bottom solution, accurately measured. The glass tank and the two capillaries are initially filled with the bulk solution, immersed in a thermostat, and allowed to come to thermal equilibrium (which is reached in 24 hours). TR is now measured. The contents of the capillary tubes can be replaced either with c_b solution or with solutions of different compositions, with the aid of 5 mL syringes provided with 25 cm stems ending in flexible "Teflon" tubes, which will not damage the platinum electrodes. The capillaries are then filled with the top and bottom solutions and allowed to diffuse into the bulk solution. Resistance ratio readings are taken at recorded times in intervals of 5 minutes, for 1000 minutes after the beginning of the experiment. At the end of the experiment, TR_∞ is re-determined by the procedure used at the beginning, i.e. by sucking out the solutions from the capillaries *in situ*, with the help of syringes, and allowing ambient solution to flow in. agreement with the earlier TR_∞ is generally excellent. All this procedure is done without removing the cell from the tank.

The diffusion coefficient is finally evaluated using a computerized linear least-squares procedure to fit the data, according with the method theory (see above section).

EXPERIMENTAL RESULTS

Isothermal diffusion in electrolyte solutions is a transport property that may give important clues to the understanding of the complex structure of those electrolyte solutions. Furthermore, and once diffusion is a very common phenomenon, experimental data on diffusion coefficients are in high demand, both from industrial areas [43-44] and from other scientific fields [30]. In fact, not only the availability of these data is very scarce [45], but also their accurate experimental measurement has been so difficult that only few research groups have managed to obtain diffusion coefficients with reasonable accuracy.

In the following tables differential isothermal diffusion coefficients of different electrolytes, measured using the open-ended conductimetric capillary cell, will be shown.

For the sake of simplicity the D values are shown as a function of electrolyte concentration and according the ionic valence of the electrolyte.

Tables 1-2 show the diffusion coefficients of different electrolytes 1:1 and 2:2, and 2:1 respectively. The mutual differential diffusion coefficients shown in these tables are average results of, at least, 3 independent measurements. The imprecision of such average result is, with few exceptions, lower than ±1 %.

Table 1A. Mutual differential diffusion coefficients D/(10^{-9} m^2 s^{-1}) of electrolytes 1:1, at 25 °C at concentrations c/(mol dm^{-3}).

CsI	D	1.867	1.891	0.005	0.008					
[46]	D	1.966	1.923	1.866	1.800					
HCl	C	0.005	0.008	0.001	0.02	0.03	0.05	0.08	0.1	
[32]	D	3.218	3.177	3.165	3.149	3.116	3.060	3.031	3.017	
KCl	C	0.001	0.002	0.003	0.005	0.008	0.01	0.05	0.1	0.2
[47-48]	D	1.964	1.983	1.985	1.963	1.945	1.891	1.893	1.894	1.830
	C	0.5	1.0							
	D	1.867	1.891							
$KClO_4$	C	0.01	0.02	0.03	0.08	0.1				
[49]	D	1.827	1.798	1.763	1.676	1.633				
KSCN	C	0.001	0.005	0.008	0.010	0.02	0.03	0.05	0.08	0.1
[50]	D	1.800	1.756	1.746	1.736	1.725	1.714	1.739	1.764	1.743
	C	0.2	0.5	1.0						
	D	1.748	1.734	1.740						
LiCl	C	0.1014	0.2000	0.2976	0.6971	0.9961				
[51]	D	1.294	1.288	1.285	1.312	1.322				
$LiClO_4$	C	0.001	0.002	0.003	0.005	0.008	0.02	0.03	0.05	0.08
[G]	D	1.208	1.277	1.292	1.312	1.298	1.313	1.362	1.343	1.360
	C	0.1								
	D	1.333								
$NaC_2H_3O_8$	C	0.003	0.008	0.01	0.02	0.03	0.05	0.08	0.1	
[47]	D	1.147	1.106	1.102	1.091	1.087	1.073	1.076	1.096	
NH_4VO_3	C	0.001	0.005	0.010	0.020	0.030	0.050			
[H]	D	1.264	1.174	1.135	1.116	1.110	1.090			

Table 1B. Mutual differential diffusion coefficients $D/(10^{-9}\ m^2\ s^{-1})$ of electrolytes 2:2, at 25 °C at concentrations $c/(mol\ dm^{-3})$.

$BeSO_4$	C	0.005	0.008	0.01	0.03	0.05	0.08	0.1	0.2	0.3
[53]	D	1.309	0.936	1.043	0.805	0.816	0.736	0.778	0.742	0.718
	C	0.5								
	D	0.668								
$CdSO_4$	C	0.001	0.002	0.003	0.005	0.008	0.01	0.02	0.03	0.05
[54]	D	0.648	0.642	0.635	0.628	0.623	0.602	0.591	0.588	0.550
	c	0.08	0.1							
	D	0.543	0.523							
$MnSO_4$	C	0.03	0.05	0.08	0.1					
[47]	D	0.565	0.525	0.525	0.501					

Table 4 shows the mutual differential diffusion coefficients of aluminium-based electrolytes, specifically chloride and nitrate aluminium (electrolytes 3:1).

The experimental diffusion coefficients, shown in Tables 1 and 2, were fitted using a polynomial equation

$$D = a_0 + a_1\, c^{1/2} + a_2\, c + a_3\, c^{3/2} + a_4\, c^2 \qquad (29)$$

Where the coefficients a_0, a_1, a_2, a_3 and a_4 are adjustable parameters.

The fits were obtained using the mean square deviation method and the quality of each fit can be assessed by the correlation coefficient (R^2), using a confidence interval of 95 %, calculated with a minimum of 4 experimental data points. Table 3 shows the coefficients a_0 to a_4 of eq. (28). They may be used to calculate values of diffusion coefficients at specified concentrations within the range of the experimental data.

In this section we have shown the experimental diffusion coefficients of electrolyte solutions obtained using the open-ended conductimetric capillary cell. More recently this technique has been used to measure the diffusion coefficients of ionic surfactants in the absence and presence of cyclodextrins. The interactions between carbohydrates with electrolytes are of both theoretical and practical importance, and can be conveniently studied using measurements of diffusion coefficients. Cyclodextrins are cyclic oligosaccharides [60-64], having a truncated cone with a hydrophilic external surface and a relatively non-polar cavity, and form inclusion complexes with a wide variety of molecules.

Table 2. Mutual differential diffusion coefficients $D/(10^{-9}\ m^2\ s^{-1})$ of electrolytes 2:1, at 25 °C at concentrations $c/(mol\ dm^{-3})$.

$BaBr_2$	C	0.001	0.002	0.003	0.005	0.008	0.010	0.020	0.030	0.050
[47]	D	0.842	0.893	0.846	0.823	0.886	0.840	0.948	1.189	1.142
	C	0.080	0.100							
	D	1.131	1.121							
$Ba(ClO_4)_2$	C	0.005	0.008	0.01	0.02	0.03	0.05	0.08	0.10	
[55]	D	1.265	1.240	1.221	1.148	1.148	1.129	1.062	1.048	
$Ca(NO_3)_2$	C	0.001	0.002	0.003	0.005	0.008	0.01	0.02	0.03	0.08
[56]	D	1.164	1.191	1.156	1.144	1.090	1.086	1.032	1.020	0.983
	C	0.1								
	D	0.973								
$CdBr_2$	C	0.001	0.002	0.003	0.005	0.010	0.020			
[47]	D	1.337	1.220	0.995	0.890	0.905	0.954			
$CdCl_2$	C	0.001	0.002	0.003	0.005	0.008	0.010	0.020	0.030	0.050
[57]	D	1.139	1.101	1.091	1.048	1.027	1.025	1.003	0.982	0.946
	C	0.080	0.100							
	D	0.921	0.902							
CdI_2	C	0.001	0.002	0.003	0.005	0.008	0.010			
[47]	D	1.203	1.194	1.186	1.075	0.933	0.869			
$Cd(NO_3)_2$	C	0.001	0.002	0.003	0.005	0.008	0.020			
[47]	D	1.035	1.020	0.993	0.971	0.951	0.970			
$CoCl_2$	C	0.001	0.003	0.005	0.008	0.01	0.05	0.1	0.2	0.3
[58]	D	1.330	1.320	1.318	1.290	1.269	1.217	1.108	1.091	1.086
$Mg(NO_3)_2$	C	0.001	0.003	0.005	0.008	0.01	0.02	0.05	0.08	0.1
[59]	D	1.118	1.155	1.166	1.145	1.084	1.059	1.080	1.052	1.020
$MnCl_2$	C	0.001	0.002	0.003	0.005	0.008	0.01			
[47]	D	1.032	0.994	0.991	0.988	0.974	0.976			
$MnSO_4$	c	0.03	0.05	0.08	0.01					
[47]	D	0.565	0.525	0.525	0.501					
$NiCl_2$	D	1.032	0.994	0.991	0.988	0.974	0.976	0.050	0.080	0.100
[47]	D	1.114	1.112	1.083	1.074	1.059	1.044	1.012	0.974	0.953

Table 3. Mutual differential diffusion coefficients $D/(10^{-9}\ m^2\ s^{-1})$ of electrolytes 3:1, at 25 °C at concentrations $c/(mol\ dm^{-3})$.

$AlCl_3$	C	0.001	0.002	0.003	0.005	0.008	0.010	0.020	0.030	0.050
[47]	D	0.158	0.255	0.319	0.401	0.477	0.493	0.602	0.630	0.716
	C	0.08	0.1							
	D	0.755	0.793							
$Al(NO_3)_3$	C	0.002	0.003	0.008	0.020	0.030	0.050	0.08	0.1	
[47]	D	0.885	0.897	0.908	0.901	0.885	0.862	0.845	0.827	

Table 4. Fitting coefficients (a_0 to a_4) of a polynomial equation to the mutual differential diffusion coefficients of different electrolytes at 25 °C. The different coefficients should be read as: $D/(m^2\ s^{-1}) = a_0+a_1(c/M)^{1/2}+a_2(c/M)+a_3(c/M)^{3/2}+a_4\ (c/M)^2$.

Electrolyte	R^2	a_0	a_1	A_2	a_3	a_4
$AlCl_3$	1.00	-1.434e-10	1.165e-8	-7.033e-8	2.093e-7	-2.338e-7
$Al(NO_3)_3$	1.00	7.965e-10	3.004e-9	-2.627e-8	8.615e-8	-1.016e-7
$BaBr_2$ a)	1.00	-1.685e-9	1.829e-7	-4.619e-6	4.886e-5	-1.845e-4
$BaBr_2$ b)	1.00	-1.436e-8	2.689e-7	-1.707e-6	4.712e-6	-4.788e-6
$Ba(ClO_4)_2$	0.98	1.629e-9	-7.999e-9	5.227e-8	-1.575e-7	1.700e-7
$BeSO_4$	0.98	2.024e-9	-1.403e-8	5.518e-8	-9.033e-8	5.167e-8
$Ca(NO_3)_2$	0.98	1.193e-9	2.029e-10	-2.207e-8	1.147e-7	-1.707e-7
$CdBr_2$	0.98	8.432e-10	5.381e-8	-1.683e-6	1.697e-5	-5.465e-5
$CdCl_2$	0.99	1.259e-9	-4.840e-9	3.549e-8	-1.238e-7	1.541e-7
CdI_2	1.00	1.285e-9	-1.140e-8	4.816e-7	-7.555e-6	3.464e-5
$Cd(NO_3)_2$	0.99	9.657e-10	6.724e-9	-1.934e-7	1.764e-6	-5.174e-6
$CdSO_4$	1.00	8.755e-10	3.317e-9	-8.062e-8	5.130e-7	-1.054e-6
$CoCl_2$	0.98	1.350e-9	-0.497e-9	1.808e-9	4.267e-9	-1.647e-9
CsI	0.99	2.052e-9	-2.762e-9	0	0	0
HCl	0.99	3.450e-9	-5.681e-9	4.276e-8	-1.588e-7	2.110e-7
KCl i)	0.99	1.323e-9	4.471e-8	-1.091e-6	1.145e-5	-4.441e-5
KCl ii)	1.00	1.895e-9	-8.165e-11	5.900e-10	-1.321e-9	8.093e-10
$KClO_4$	1.00	1.480e-9	9.227e-9	-8.219e-8	2.808e-7	-3.426e-7
KSCN*	0.98	1.824e-9	-5.707e-10	-9.324e-9	7.695e-8	-1.400e-7
KSCN**	1.00	1.644e-9	5.866e-10	-1.031e-9	5.411e-10	0
KSCN*	0.98	1.824e-9	-5.707e-10	-9.324e-9	7.695e-8	-1.400e-7
KSCN**	1.00	1.644e-9	5.866e-10	-1.031e-9	5.411e-10	0
LiCl	1.00	1.168e-9	1.123e-9	-3.456e-9	4.237e-9	-1.750e-9
$LiClO_4$ c)	0.98	1.997e-9	-9.577e-9	1.257e-7	-7.244e-7	1.576e-6
$LiClO_4$ d)	1.00	2.780e-9	1.280e-8	5.213e-8	-6.998e-8	0
$Mg(NO_3)_2$ x)	1.00	7.909e-10	2.207e-8	-5.395e-7	6.200e-6	-2.718e-5
$Mg(NO_3)_2$ y)	1.00	1.723e-9	-1.360e-8	9.832e-8	-2.931e-7	3.035e-7
$MnCl_2$	1.00	1.642e-9	-4.018e-8	9.118e-7	-8.986e-6	3.219e-5
$MnSO_4$	1.00	2.132e-9	-1.950e-8	7.852e-8	-1.049e-7	0
$NaC_2H_3O_8$	0.99	1.309e-9	-4.651e-9	3.772e-8	-1.376e-7	1.837e-7
$NiCl_2$	0.99	1.203e-9	-2.768e-9	2.194e-8	-8.387e-8	1.084e-7
NH_4VO_3	1.00	1.399e-9	-4.175e-9	2.766e-8	-5.596e-8	0

* 0.001 c 0.1; ** 0.1 c 1.0; a) 0.001 c 0.01 b) 0.02 c 0.1; c) 0.001 c 0.03; d) 0.03 c 0.1; i) 0.001 c 0.01; ii) 0.01 c 1.0; x) 0.001 c 0.01 y) 0.01 c 0.1.

Surfactants are used in a wide range of applications, in areas as diverse as detergents, paints paper coatings, food and pharmacy [65-69]. We are interested in the behaviour of ionic surfactants in these systems. Both the α- and β-cyclodextrins have the ability to form 1:1 inclusion complexes with sodium dodecylsulfate (SDS). To study the interactions in the complex with β-CD, experimental data have been obtained for differential diffusion coefficients of SDS in aqueous solutions at 298.15 K over the concentration range 0.0010 –

0.0817 M alone and in the presence of different concentrations of the cyclodextrin using the previously reported open-ended capillary cell [70]. From this research, we have obtained some information concerning the competition between the binding of surfactant molecules to cyclodextrins and that to their own micellar aggregates upon addition of β-CD, and to see how this affects the diffusion for this electrolyte above and below the critical micelle concentration.

DISCUSSION

It is well known that the structure of electrolyte solutions is very complex. They lack the order of the solid state or the independence and freedom of movement of the entities of the gaseous state and consequently it is not so easy to treat mathematically electrolyte solutions as solids or gases. Furthermore, electrolytes in a solvent are subject to electric interactions difficult to account in any model attempting to describe this structure.

The calculation of diffusion coefficients from equations based on some models describing the movement of matter in electrolyte solutions, is, in the end, a process contributing to the knowledge of their structure, provided we have accurate and precise experimental data to test these equations.

Assuming that each ion of diffusing electrolyte can be regarded as moving under the influence of two forces, i) a gradient of the chemical potential for that ionic species, and ii) an electrical field produced by the motion of oppositely charged ions, we come up to the Nernst-Hartley equation [2]

$$D = [(\nu_1+\nu_2)\,\lambda_1^0\,\lambda_2^0 / (\nu_1\,|Z_1|\,(\lambda_1^0 + \lambda_2^0))]\,(R\,T / F^2)\,[1 + (d\ln\gamma_\pm / d\ln c)] \quad (30)$$

where λ^0 are the limiting ionic conductivities of the ions (subscripts 1 and 2 for cation and anion, respectively), Z is the algebraic valence of the ion, ν is the number of ions formed upon complete ionisation of one solute "molecule", T is the absolute temperature, R and F are the gas and Faraday constants, respectively, and $\gamma_\pm$ is the mean molar activity coefficient.

Equation (30) is often written as

$$D = D^0\,[1 + (d\ln\gamma_\pm / d\ln c)] \quad (31)$$

where D^0 is the Nernst limiting value of the diffusion coefficient.

Onsager and Fuoss [71], improved eq. (31) by taking into account the electrophoretic effects (eq. 32):

$$D = (D^0 + \Sigma\Delta_n)[1 + (d\ln\gamma_\pm / d\ln c)] \quad (32)$$

The difference between eqs. (31) and (32) can be found in the electrophoretic term, Δ_n, given by

$$\Delta_n = K_B\,T\,A_n\,(Z_1^n\,t_2^0 + Z_2^n\,t_1^0)^2 / (a^n\,|Z_1\,Z_2|) \quad (33)$$

where K_B is the Boltzmann's constant, A_n are functions of the dielectric constant, of the viscosity of the solvent, of the temperature, and of the dimensionless concentration-dependent quantity (κ *a*), being the reciprocal of average radius of the ionic atmosphere; t_1^0 and t_2^0 are the limiting transport numbers of the cation and anion, respectively.

Since the expression for the electrophoretic effect has been derived on the basis of the expansion of the exponential Boltzmann function because that function had been consistent with the Poisson equation, we only, in major cases, would have to take into account the electrophoretic term of the first order (n=1). For symmetrical electrolytes we can consider the second term. Thus, the experimental data can be compared with the calculated D on the basis of eqs. (34) and (35)

$$D = (D^0 + \Delta_1 + \Delta_2)\,[1 + c\,(d\ln\gamma_\pm / dc)] \quad (34)$$

$$D = (D^0 + \Delta_1)\,[1 + c\,(d\ln\gamma_\pm / dc)] \quad (35)$$

for symmetrical and non-symmetrical electrolytes, respectively.

The theory of mutual diffusion in binary electrolytes, developed by Pikal [72], includes the Onsager-Fuoss equation, but has new terms resulting from the application of the Boltzmann exponential function for the study of diffusion.

The electrophoretic correction appears as the sum of two terms

$$\Delta v_j = \Delta v_j^L + \Delta v_j^S \quad (36)$$

where Δv_j^L represents the effect of electrostatic interactions of long-range, and Δv_j^S represents them as short-range.

Designating by $M = 10^{12}$ L/c the solute thermodynamic mobility, where L is the thermodynamic diffusion coefficient, ΔM can be represented by the equation

$$(1 / M) = (1 / M^0)\,(1 - (\Delta M / M^0)) \quad (37)$$

where M^0 is the value of M for infinitesimal concentration, and

$$\Delta M = \Delta M^{0F} + \Delta M_1 + \Delta M_2 + \Delta M_A + \Delta M_{H1} + \Delta M_{H2} + \Delta M_{H3} \quad (38)$$

The first term on the right hand in eq. (38), ΔM^{0F}, represents the Onsager-Fuoss term for the effect of the concentration in the solute thermodynamic mobility, M; the second term, ΔM_1, is a consequence of the approximation applied on the ionic thermodynamic force; the other terms result from the Boltzmann exponential function.

The relation between the solute thermodynamic mobility and the mutual diffusion coefficient is given by

$$D = (L / c)\,10^3\,R\,T\,\nu\,[1 + c\,(d\ln\gamma_\pm / dc)] \quad (39)$$

From eqs. (39) and (37) a version of Pikal's equation (eq. 40) is obtained

$$D = \frac{1}{\frac{1}{M^0}\left(1 - \frac{\Delta M}{M^0}\right)} \left(10^3 R T \nu\right) \left[1 + c \left(d \ln\gamma_\pm / d c\right)\right] \quad (40)$$

Data from these models for different type of electrolytes in dilute aqueous solutions are present in the literature [73-74]. As an example, Figures 2-4 compare experimental results with the curves drawn on the basis of Onsager-Fuoss and Pikal models. We see that for symmetrical uni-univalent (Fig.2) both theories give similar results and they are consistent with experimental results. In fact, if Pikal's theory is valid, ΔM^{0F} must be the major term, all other terms are much smaller and they partially cancel each other. Concerning symmetrical but polyvalent electrolytes (e.g. Fig. 3), we can well see that Pikal's theory is a better approximation than the Onsager-Fuoss. In polyvalent non-symmetrical electrolytes (e.g. Fig. 4), agreement between experimental data and Pikal calculations is not so good, eventually because of the full use of Boltzmann's exponential in Pikal's development.

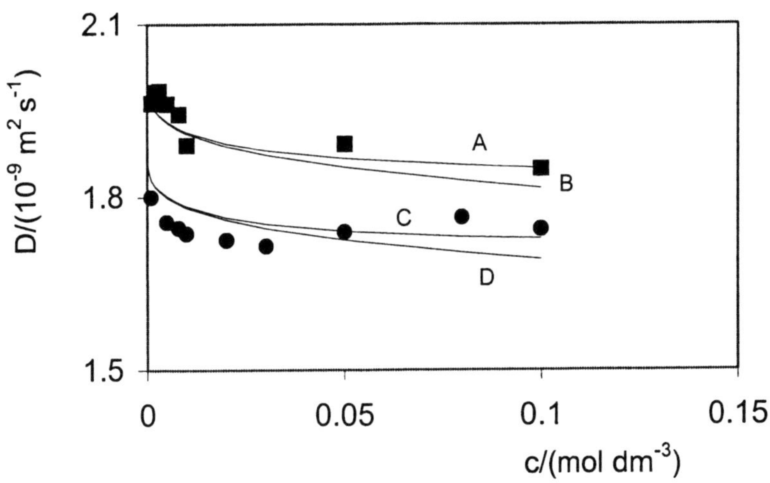

Figure 2. Comparison of diffusion coefficients of KCl-H_20 [35] and KSCN—H_2O [50] with Onsager-Fuoss (curves A and C, respectively) and Pikal models (curves B and D, respectively), and our results (for KCl; for KSCN) at 298.15 K.

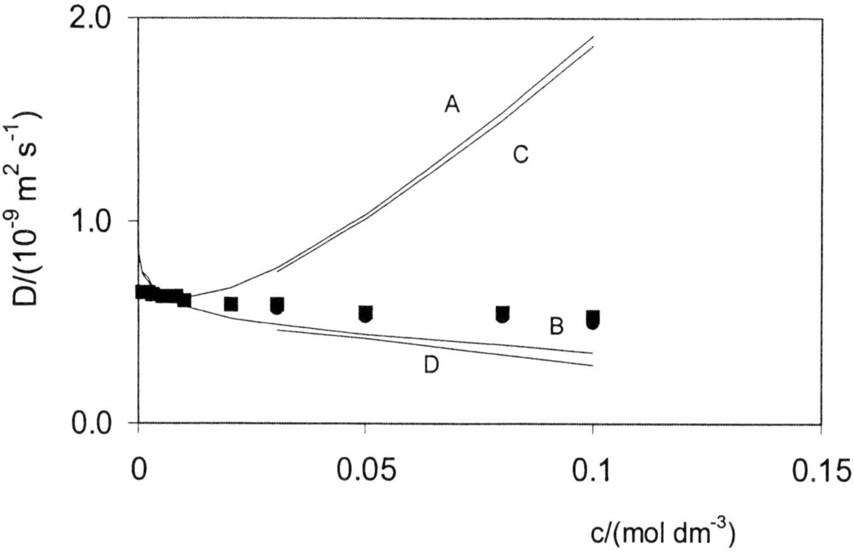

Figure 3. Comparison of diffusion coefficients of $CdSO_4$—H_2O and $MnSO_4$-H_20 with Onsager-Fuoss (curves A and C, respectively), and Pikal models (curves B, and D, respectively), and our results (for $CdSO_4$;   for $MnSO_4$) at 298.15 K.

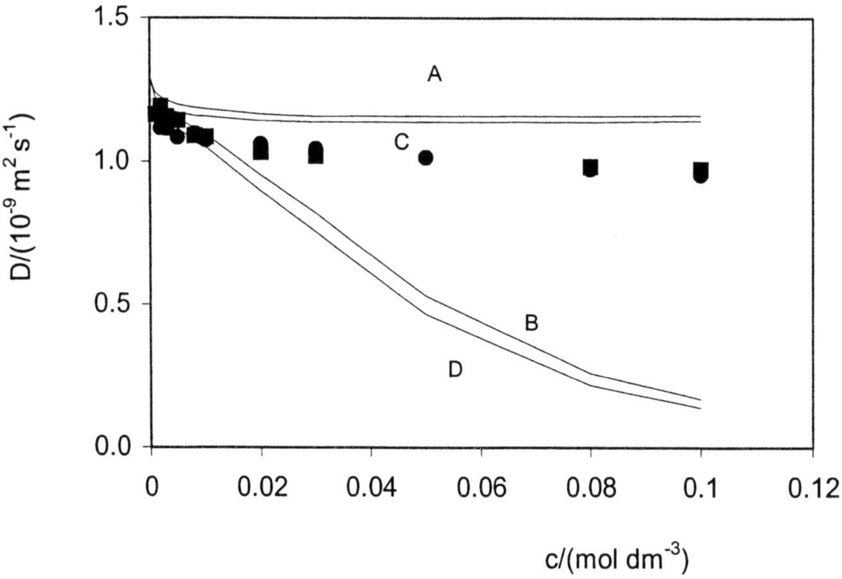

Figure 4. Comparison of diffusion coefficients of $Ca(NO_3)_2$—H_2O and $NiCl_2$-H_20 with Onsager-Fuoss (curves A and C, respectively), and Pikal models (curves B, and D, respectively), and our results (for $Ca(NO_3)_2$;   for $NiCl_2$) at 298.15.

In conclusion, no theory on diffusion in electrolyte solutions is capable of giving generally reliable data concerning the magnitude of the diffusion coefficient D. However, for estimating purposes when no experimental data is available, we can to use the Onsager-Fuoss equation (Eq. 34) for symmetrical uni-univalent electrolytes (1:1) in aqueous dilute solutions (or Pikal's eq. (40) once the results are similar). For symmetrical polyvalent electrolytes (e.g. 2:2) we use the Pikal equation (eq. 34). For non-symmetrical electrolytes, despite of the reasonable agreement, in some cases, between the experimental results and the calculated from the Onsager's equation (Fig. 4), in general cases [74].], we can see more agreement between our results and those obtained by equation (35). Thus, we can conclude the actual value should lie between the values calculated from those models.

For higher concentrations (c > 0.01 M), our experimental data and those from other researchers are in good agreement, but the results from the above models differ considerably from experimental observation (see ref [58]). This is not surprising if we take into account the formation of complexes and the variety of ion pairs eventually formed, the change with concentration of parameters such as viscosity, dielectric constant and hydration, factors not taken into account in Onsager-Fuoss and Pikal models. For example, for solutions of cobalt chloride at higher concentrations ($c > 0.08$ mol dm^{-3}) (Fig. 5), the results predicted from the Onsager-Fuoss model differ significantly from experimental observation. In this context, taking only in consideration the effect of the viscosity on diffusion of this electrolyte in Gordon equation (eq. 41 [75]), we obtain results closer to experimental data. We can conclude that the behaviour of this electrolyte depends strongly on the viscosity change in the solution.

$$D_G = D_{OF}\left(\frac{\eta_0}{\eta}\right), \qquad (41)$$

η is the viscosity of the solution.

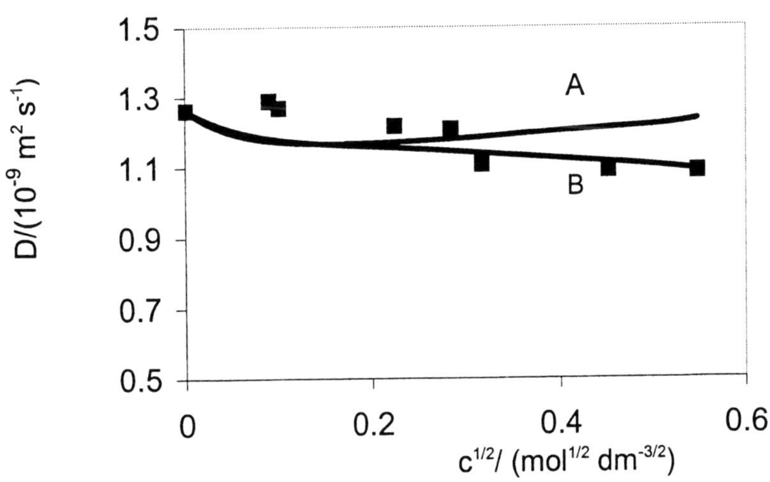

Figure 5. Comparison of diffusion coefficients of $CoCl_2$ calculated by Onsager-Fuoss and Gordon models (curves A and B, respectively), and our results ( ) at 298.15 K [58].

ACKNOWLEDGEMENTS:

Financial support from POCTI/QUI/39593/2001 is gratefully acknowledged.

REFERENCES

1. B. Clark, *Proc. Phys. Soc.* 36 (1924) 313.
2. R. A. Robinson, R.H. Stokes. *Electrolyte solutions*. 2nd Ed., Butterworths: London, 1959.
3. G.L. Gouy, *Comp. Rend.* 90 (1880) 307.
4. R.H. Stokes, *J. Am. Chem. Soc.*, 73 (1951) 3527.
5. H.S. Harned, D.M. French, *Ann. N.Y. Acad. Sci.* 46 (1945) 267.
6. H.S. Harned, C.L. Hildreth, *J. Am. Chem. Soc.* 73 (1951) 650.
7. H.S. Harned, R.L. Nuttall, *J. Am. Chem. Soc.* 71 (1949) 1460.
8. H.S. Harned, M. Blander, *J. Am. Chem. Soc.* 75 (1953) 2853.
9. H.S. Harned, R.M. Hudson, *J. Am. Chem. Soc.* 73 (1951) 652.
10. H.S. Harned, C.L. Hildreth, *J. Am. Chem. Soc.* 73 (1951) 3292.
11. H.S. Harned, F.M. Polestra, *J.Am. Chem. Soc.* 76 (1954) 2064.
12. H.S. Harned, A.L. Levy, *J. Am. Chem. Soc.* 71 (1949) 2781.
13. H.S. Harned, F.M. Polestra, *J. Am. Chem. Soc.* 75 (1953) 4168.
14. H.S. Harned, C.C. Blake, *J. Am. Chem. Soc.* 73 (1951) 2448.
15. H.S. Harned, C.C. Blake, *J. Am. Chem. Soc.* 73 (1951) 5882.
16. H.S. Harned, R.M. Hudson, *J. Am. Chem. Soc.* 73 (1951) 5880.
17. H.S. Harned, R.M. Hudson, *J. Am. Chem. Soc.* 73 (1951) 3781.
18. H.S. Harned, C.C. Blake, *J. Am. Chem. Soc.* 73 (1951) 4255.
19. H.S. Harned, R.M. Hudson, *J. Am. Chem. Soc.* 73 (1951) 5083.
20. H.S. Harned, M. Blander, C.L. Hildreth, *J. Am. Chem. Soc.* 76 (1954) 4219.
21. H.S. Harned, J.A. Shropshire, *J. Am. Chem. Soc.* 80 (1958) 2618, 2967.
22. H.S. Harned, H.W. Parker, M. Blander, *J. Am. Chem. Soc.* 77 (1955) 2071.
23. H.S. Harned, H.W. Parker, *J. Am. Chem. Soc.* 77 (1955) 265.
24. R.H. Stokes, *J. Am. Chem. Soc.* 72 (1950) 763.
25. V.M.M. Lobo, *Gold Medal for V.M.M. Lobo's diffusion cell at the 15th International Exhibition of Inventions and New Techniques*, Geneva, 3-12 April, 1987.
26. J.G. Albright, R. Mills, *J. Phys. Chem.* 69 (1965) 3120.
27. R. Mills, V.M.M. Lobo. *Self-diffusion in electrolyte solution. A critical examination of data compiled from the literature*. Elsevier: Amsterdam, 1989.
28. J.A. Harpst, E. Holt, P.A. Lyon, *J.Am. Chem. Soc.* 69 (1965) 2341.
29. H.S. Harned, R.L. Nuttal, *J. Am. Chem. Soc.* 69 (1947) 736.
30. H.J.V. Tyrrell, K.R. Harris. *Diffusion in liquids: a theoretical and experimental study*. Butterworths: London, 1984.
31. J. Agar, V.M.M. Lobo, *J. Chem. Soc. Faraday Trans. I*, 71, (1975) 1659.
32. V.M.M. Lobo. *Diffusion and thermal diffusion in solutions of electrolytes*. Ph.D. Thesis, Cambridge, 1971.
33. J. Crank. *The mathematics of diffusion*. 2nd ed., Oxford Univ. Press: Oxford, 1999.
34. A.J.M. Valente. *Diffusion of electrolytes in aqueous solutions and in hydrogels with different degrees of hydrophilicity*, Ph.D. Thesis, Coimbra, 1999.

35. V.M.M. Lobo, A.C.F. Ribeiro, L.M.P. Verissimo, *J. Molec. Liq.* 78 (1998) 139.
36. J.H. Wang, *J. Am. Chem. Soc.* 74 (1952) 1182.
37. J.E. Burkell, J.W.T. Spinks, *Can. J. Chem.* 30 (1952) 311.
38. C.J. Kraus, J.W.T. Spinks, *Can. J. Chem.* 32 (1954) 71.
39. J.H. Wang, *J. Am. Chem. Soc.* 73 (1951) 510.
40. E. Berne, J. Berggren, *Acta Chem. Scand.* 14 (1960) 428.
41. V.M.M. Lobo, A.C.F. Ribeiro, A.J.M. Valente, *Corros. Prot. Mat.* 14 (1995) 14.
42. H. Tennekes, J.L. Lunley. *A first course in turbulence.* MIT Press: Cambridge, 1972.
43. E.L. Cussler. *Diffusion: mass transfer in fluid systems.* Cambridge University Press: Cambridge, 1984.
44. A.L. Horvath. *Handbook of aqueous electrolyte solutions. Physical properties. Estimation and correlation methods.* John Wiley and Sons: New York, 1985.
45. V.M.M. Lobo. *Handbook of electrolyte solutions.* Elsevier: Amsterdam, 1990.
46. V.M.M. Lobo, J.L. Quaresma. *Diffusion coefficients in aquoeus solutions of cesium iodide.* 1st Meeting of the Electrochemistry Portuguese Society, Coimbra, 1984.
47. V.M.M. Lobo, *Pure Appl. Chem.* 65 (1993) 2613.
48. V.M.M. Lobo, A.J.M. Valente, *Port. Electrochim. Acta* 14 (1996) 133.
49. V.M.M. Lobo, M.H. Teixeira, J.L. Quaresma, *Electrochim. Acta* 27 (1982) 1509.
50. A.C.F. Ribeiro, V.M.M. Lobo, J.J.S. Natividade, *J. Molec. Liq.* 94 (2001) 61.
51. A.J.M. Valente, V.M.M. Lobo, *Port. Electrochim. Acta* 18 (2000) 159.
52. A.C.F. Ribeiro, V.M.M. Lobo, E.F.G. Azevedo, *J. Sol. Chem.* 30 (2002) 1111.
53. V.M.M. Lobo, A.C.F. Ribeiro, L.M.P. Verissimo, *J. Chem. Eng. Data* 39 (1994) 726.
54. V.M.M. Lobo, J.L. Quaresma. *Diffusion coefficients in aqueous solutions of cadmium sulfate.* 6th Meeting of the Portuguese Chemical Soc., Aveiro, 1983.
55. V.M.M. Lobo, J.L. Quaresma. *Diffusion coefficients in aqueous solutions of barium perchlorate.* 9th Meeting of the Portuguese Chemical Soc., Coimbra, 1986.
56. V.M.M. Lobo, J.L. Quaresma. *Diffusion coefficients in aqueous solutions of calcium nitrate.* 2nd Meeting of the Electrochemistry Portuguese Society, Ofir, 1986.
57. V.M.M. Lobo, J.L. Quaresma, *Electrochim. Acta* 35 (1990) 1433.
58. A.C.F. Ribeiro, V.M.M. Lobo, J.J.S. Natividade, *J. Chem. Eng. Data* 47 (2002) 539.
59. V.M.M. Lobo, J.L. Quaresma. *Diffusion coefficients in aqueous solutions of manganese chloride.* 7th Meeting of the Portuguese Chemical Soc., Lisboa, 1986.
60. S. Li, W.C. Purdy, *Chem. Rev.* 92 (1992) 1457.
61. V.T. Livery, G. Cavallaro, G. Giammona, G. Pitarresi, G. Puglisi, C. Ventura, *Thermochimica Acta* 99 (1992) 125.
62. O. Ortona, L. Paduano, L. Costantino, V. Vitagliano, *J. Molec. Liq.* 63 (1995) 291.
63. W. Saenger, J. Jacob, K. Gessler, T. Steiner, D. Hoffmann, H. Sanbe, K. Koizumi, S.M. Smith, T. Takaha, *Chem. Rev.* 98 (1998) 1787.
64. K. Uekama, F. Hirayama, T. Irie, *Chem. Rev.* 98 (1998) 2045.
65. B. Jonsson, B. Lindman, K. Holmberg, B. Kronberg. *Surfactants and polymers in aqueous solution.* John Wiley: New York, 1998.
66. A.J.M. Valente, A.Ya. Polishchuk, V.M.M. Lobo, H.D. Burrows, *Langmuir* 16 (2000) 6475;
67. D.F. Evans, S. Mukherjee, D.J. Mitchell, B.W. Ninham, *J. Colloid Interface Sci.* 93 (1983) 184.
68. D.G. Leaist, L. Hao, *J. Chem. Soc. Faraday Trans.* 91 (1995) 2837.

69. Z. Deng, H. Lu, D.G. Leaist, *J. Chem. Eng. Data* 41 (1996) 214.
70. A.C.F. Ribeiro, V.M.M. Lobo, E.F.G. Azevedo, M.G. Miguel, H.D. Burrows, J. Molec. Liq. In press.
71. L. Onsager, R.M. Fuoss, *J. Phys. Chem.* 36 (1932) 2689.
72. M.J. Pikal, *J. Phys. Chem.* 75 (1971) 663.
73. V.M.M. Lobo, A.C.F. Ribeiro, S.G.C.S. Andrade, *Ber. Buns. Phys. Chem.* 99 (1995) 713.
74. V.M.M. Lobo, A.C.F. Ribeiro, S.G.C.S. Andrade, *Port. Electrochim. Acta* 14 (1996) 45.
75. A.R. Gordon, *J. Chem. Phys.* 5 (1937) 522.

Chapter 3

1,4–TRANS–POLYDIENES[1]

Yu.B. Monakov, I.R. Mullagaliev, E.Yu. Kharitonova
Institute of Organic Chemistry Ufa Scientific Center
Russian Academy of Sciences
pr. Oktyabrya 71, Ufa, 450054 Russia

ABSTRACT

The data on *trans*-polymerization of conjugated dienes (butadiene, isoprene, *cis*- and *trans*-isomers of piperylene, chloroprene) by radical, ion and ion-coordinating mechanisms are considered. The factors that forward to formation of 1,4-*trans*-structures in polydienes macromolecules are analyzed. The main attention was given to the catalysts of Ziegler-Natta type: to the influence of transition and nontransition metals nature, conditions of catalytic complexes preparation and polymerization on activity and *trans*-stereospecificity of catalysts, and molecular characteristics of forming polydienes. The correlation between monomer nature and polydienes properties is shown. Application fields for *trans*-polymers of butadiene, isoprene, pentadiene and chloroprene are presented.

Key Words: 1,4-*trans*-polydienes, *trans*-polymerization, polymerization catalysts, Ziegler–Natta catalytic systems, conjugated dienes, 1,4-*trans*-polybutadiene, 1,4-*trans*-polyisoprene 1,4-*trans*—polypentadiene, polychloroprene.

INTRODUCTION

Conjugated dienes can form polymers with various microstructure. Even simple representative butadiene is able to polymerize either by one, or by both double bonds. By this, macromolecules with different microstructure are formed: 1,4-*trans*-, 1,4-*cis*-, 1,2-, and 1,2-units may be in iso- or sindio-positions in polymer chain. Dienes with side substituents have possibility to form polymers with more microstructure combinations, and macromolecules

[1] This work was supported by the Russian Foundation for Basic Research, project no. 02-03-33315, and the Foundation for Support of Scientific Schools, RFBS project no. 00-15-97322.

structure may be complicated by connection with monomer molecules not only by "head-to-tail", but also "head-to-head" and "tail-to-tail" types.

Polydienes with regular microstructure in which monomer units are connected by "head-to-tail" type have practical importance in the first place. 1,4-*cis*- and 1,4-*trans*-polyisoprene (PI) (synthetic analogues of natural rubber and gutta-percha), 1,4-*cis*-PB, 1,4-*trans*-polychloroprene (PCP) are the most widely used materials.

Among all famous methods of conjugated dienes polymerization (radical, cationic, anionic, anion-coordinating) only ion-coordinating catalysis in the presence of Ziegler-Natta systems can form macromolecules with high stereoregularity and regular units connection. At the same time, types of polymerization initiation mentioned above are used in industrial production of important polymers containing in their structure noticeable amount of 1,4-*trans*-polydienes units. It concerns PCP from homopolymers, and from copolymers it regards to butadiene-nitryl, butadiene-styrene rubbers that are obtained with the use of radical initiators. Pentadiene oligomers containing *trans*-units in the main, are received for lacquer-dye industry with the use of cationic initiating systems.

Further, we shall consider homopolymerization of four the most important dienes (butadiene, isoprene, pentadiene and chloroprene) in the presence of radical, cationic and anionic catalysts with the aim to show their possibilities in *trans*-structures formation.

RADICAL POLYMERIZATION

Under radical polymerization dienes have nearly the same row of relative reaction ability as under anionic: monomer activity reduces in the row chloroprene–butadiene–isoprene–2,3-dimethylbutadiene–cyclohexadiene [1]. The characteristic feature of dienes behavior under radical initiation is dependence of polymers microstructure on conformation of monomers in solution. It is known, that the biggest part of molecules of indicated dienes are in transoid conformation, especially at low temperatures [2]. As the result, radical polymerization leads to the formation of polydienes with predominant content of *trans*-1,4-units that depends on polymerization temperature (table 1) [1]. Under polymerization of nonsymmetrical dienes appearance of structural heterogeneity is possible because of monomer connection by not only "head-to-tail" type. For isoprene possibilities of macroradical attack on C_1 and C_4 are close – nearly equal quantity of 1,2- and 3,4-units is formed. In the case of piperylene low amount of side vinyl groups in polymer indicating about connection of diene to the propagating polymer chain mainly with participation of nonscreened C_1 atom. It was shown, that *cis*-isomer of piperylene is polymerized by radical mechanism more actively than *trans*-isomer, and they suggest that in both cases insertion of monomers to the polymer chain occurs out of their transoid conformation [3]. Polymers contain 56-59% of 1,4-*trans*-, 15-17% of 1,4-*cis*-, 16-20% of 1,2-*trans*-, 7-10% of 1,2-*cis*- and 0% of 3,4-units. Irregularity of radical polypentadiene (PPD) structure is intensified by the availability of various types of 1,4-units connection; the following distribution of diads was determined for them: 79,9% of 1,4–1,4 connection, 13,8% of 1,4–4,1 and 6,3% of 4,1–1,4 connections [4].

Thus, for the reception of stereoregular polymers by radical polymerization of dienes (except chloroprene) additional coordinating factors are needed. With them may be reckon

E-mail: *monakov@anrb.ru* (Monakov Yurii Borisovich)

preliminary orientation of monomer molecules in canal complexes of some crystal compounds (urea, thiourea, perhydrotriphenilene, desoxycholic and apocholic acids) [5]. Naturally, polymerization rate (that is usually initiated by γ-radiation) and microstructure of polymer depend on relation between dienes and canals sizes. So, in relatively wide canals of desoxycholic acid butadiene forms polymer containing 73% of 1,4-*trans*- and 27% of 1,2-units [6]. In work [7] butadiene coordination was carried out by introduction of $RhCl_3$: varying the concentration of the last one from 0 to 0,4% one can change 1,4-*trans*-units content in polymer from 64% to 100%. Polymerization rate by this significantly reduces at the expense of inhibiting action of rhodium salt on initiating process. They suppose that under mentioned conditions polymerization has as radical, so coordination character.

As in the cases of butadiene and isoprene the only method of highstereoregular 1,4-*trans*-PPD synthesis is inclusion polymerization that is usually initiated by radiation, by sometimes the use of substance initiators is possible [8]. Specific orientation of diene molecules in canals of urea, for example, and their readiness by this for polymerization lead to PPD radiation-chemical yield that is twice as much in comparison with polymerization in mass. Preference of 1,4-*trans*-units was shown out of juxtaposition of sizes of 1,2-*trans*-configuration units and canals diameter in urea complexes.

The formation of only 1,4-*trans*-PPD under 1,3-*trans*-pentadiene polymerization in perhydrotriphenilene canals is the example of noticeable influence of canal complex nature on polymer parameters [9]. Under polymerization of desoxycholic acid complexes with various pentadiene isomers *cis*-isomer gives more stereoregular polymer than *trans*-isomer (97 and 91% of 1,4-*trans*-units). They suggested that it is associated with more strong orientation action of matrix canal sides on *cis*-pentadiene molecules [10]. Indeed, substitution of desoxycholic acid by apocholic acid that forms canals of large sizes leads to the decrease of 1,4-*trans*-units content in polymer down to 85% [8].

In spite of limitations mentioned above radical polymerization is widely used in industry for reception of dienes homo- and copolymers with predominant content of *trans*-units. First of all it regards to butadiene-styrene and butadiene-nitryl rubbers, PCP. We shall limit ourselfs to PCP synthesis not to come out of the review scope that is devoted to *trans*-homopolymers and *trans*-copolymers of dienes.

The main industry method of chloroprene rubber reception is emulsion polymerization by radical mechanism in the presence of organic and inorganic peroxides, salts of metals of variable valence, various oxidation-reduction initiating systems [11-13]. For synthesis of linear PCP the use of molecular mass regulators is necessary, the main chain transmitters are sulfur, mercaptans, alkylxantohendisulfides [11]. High polarity of chloroprene molecule forwards firstly to monomer existence predominantly in transoid conformation at the moment of insertion into polymer chain without additional coordinating (stereoregulating) factor; secondly, to predominant units orientation in polymer in 1,4–1,4 positions. At the same time, as already said above under radical diene polymerization, including chloroprene, temperature increase reduces 1,4-*trans*-units content in polymer. The temperature of 40°C in industry is regarded to be optimal; forming by this linear crystal α–PCP contains 85-90% of 1,4-*trans*-, 8-12% of 1,4-*cis*- and 2-3% of 1,2-units [32]. Content of crystal phase in PCP synthesized at 0, 10, 40 and 55°C is 30, 25, 15 and 8% at room temperature, accordingly. Crystalline degree of polymers synthesized in the presence of mercaptanes is generally higher than of rubbers received with sulfur and tetraethylthiuramdisulfide [15].

Cationic Polymerization

Relative reaction ability of different dienes in cationic polymerization process increases with the rise of electron-donor substituents number or with the reduce of their electron-seeking, for example in row chloroprene–butadiene–isoprene–pentadiene–2,3-dimethylbutadiene [16]. Polydienes contain in their chains mainly 1,4-*trans*-units (in the linear part) and *cis*-structures are practically absent [17, 18]. The last one may be associated as with the low polymerization temperature in typically cationic systems, so with the facility of *cis-trans*-isomerisation of units in polymer chain [19]. Diene polymerization occurs on any cationic catalysts, for example Fridel-Krafts, Lyuis acids [20], and also under γ–radiation with the use of natural or synthetic aluminumsilicates [16].

Characteristic feature of diene cationic polymerization is the ability of inside double bonds of forming macromolecules for further interaction with catalyst resulting in cycle structures formation. It leads to reduce of polydienes unsaturation, that increases a little in the row: PB – 13-70%, PI – 15-80%, PPD – 60-90% [17, 18, 20, 21], this coincides with relative activities of dienes in polymerization. Cyclic structures content decreases under polymerization temperature reduce and using solvent polarity increase. Reduced unsaturation may be also associated with chain transfer on polymer with branches formation [20, 22]. Low molecular mass of polymers under cationic polymerization is conditioned by significant role of reaction of chain transfer on monomer (it increases with the rise of catalysts acidity) and solvent (reduces with the increase of polarity of the last one) [16]. This is the distinctive feature of cationic processes in contrast to radical and anionic.

The facts set before show the failure of cationic catalysts application for reception of highmolecular and highstereoregular polydienes, including 1,4-*trans*-polymers. Products of only one diene cationic polymerization (pentadiene) are of practical interest, as lacquer-dye material for example [16]. It is the most active monomer, and role of crosslinking and cyclization processes in the course of its cationic polymerization is significantly lesser than in the case of butadiene and especially isoprene because of the bigger stability of propagating macrocation end [23]. This is positively influence on unsaturation of PPD.

High monomer conversion and possibility of molecular mass regulation are the advantages of cationic polymerization as a method of oligopentadiene synthesis. So, high rates of pentadiene polymerization are observed on $TiCl_4$ with water additives in toluene. Molecular mass of the product is 400-1800, the unsaturation achieves 78%, linear part of oligopentadiene contains mainly 1,4-*trans*- (73%) and 1,2-units (20%). The yield, unsaturation and molecular mass are lower in the case of *cis*-isomer of pentadiene-1,3 [23]. Oligopentadiene received with the help of BF_3 is characterized by 95% of 1,4-*trans*-units and molecular mass 860 [24]. It is rather preferable to use high active soluble etherates of $AlCl_3$ as initiators, with the help of which it is possible to develop new technologies of oligopentadiene production with application of tubular turbulent reactors [25].

Anionic Polymerization

Relative activity of dienes under anionic polymerization reduces with the rise of electron density in the monomer's conjugated double bonds system when you introduce corresponding electron-donor substituents. It is characteristic that several active sites types may participate in propagating reactions. These types may be different not only in their reaction ability, but also in their regio- and stereospecificity of action. Dynamic equilibrium between sites depends on nature of the anion, cation, solvent and temperature, polydienes microstructure is very sensitive to reagents structure and polymerization conditions [26].

They regard that *trans*-connection of dienes on alkali catalysts occurs on associated active sites, in contrast to *cis*-polymerization [27]. Monomer structure influences not only on polymerization rate, but also on macromolecule chain structure. On the base of investigation of 1- and 2-sabstituted alkylbutadienes polymerization in the presence of lithium initiators it was shown that polymers of dienes of the first row contain more 1,4-*trans*-units, especially with the increase of electron density at first carbon atom (C_1) of monomer. Thus, polymers of *trans*-pentadiene, 1-phenyl and 1,1'-dimethylbutadiene contain 44, 58 and 87% of 1,4-*trans*-units, and in the last case polydiene doesn't contain 1,4-*cis*-units and destructions of "head-to-head" and "tail-to-tail" types connections [28].

The lower rate of propagation of macromolecules from *cis*-isomer in comparison with *trans*-isomer [29] and unstereospecificity of catalysts action mentioned above are the general features of anionic polymerization. So, from *trans*-pentadiene-1,3 the polymer containing 54% of 1,4-*trans*- and 9,5% of 1,2-*trans*-structures is formed; in the case of *cis*-isomer the contents of noticed units are 68 and 10,5%, accordingly [4, 30].

Speaking about the influence of catalyst nature on polymers microstructure it must be noted that in hydrocarbon mediums metals of the II group are more able to initiate 1,4-*trans*-connection of dienes units than alkali metals (except lithium) [31]. The further reduce of active sites polarity by use of mixed compounds of alkali-earth metals with zinc- or aliminumalkyls for example, independently on s-element nature allows to receive 1,4-*trans*-polydienes [32-35].

Thus, there are only separate examples of synthesis of some substituted polydienes with predominant content of 1,4-*trans*-units in the presence of anionic initiators.

Trans-Polydienes Synthesis with the Use of Cyclic Monomers

Polymers analogues to 1,4-polydienes by their structure, including those with *trans*-configuration of units may be produced from cyclic olefines, so it is not necessary to use monomers with conjugated double bonds only. Thus, polymer that is analogue of PB was obtained on Ziegler type catalysts under cyclobutene polymerization with opening of ring [36, 37]. It was shown that polymerization occurs only under the action of catalysts of coordinating type. Activity of the last ones is determined by transition metal nature mainly: derivatives of Ti, V, Cr and W are the most active, less active are derivatives of Mo, Y, U, Mn, Fe and Co are inactive. By this opening of ring occurs only in the presence of catalysts on the base of Ti, W and Mo in combination with organic derivatives of nontransition elements of I–IV groups (Li, Mg, Al, Si). Later it was shown that in the case of vanadium catalysts it is possible to regulate the direction of cyclbutene polymerization varying organometallic cocatalyst nature. Thus, VCl_4 in combination with $Al(Et)_3$ forms polymer with 99% of cyclic units, and with *n*-BuLi it gives only unsaturated polymer with equal amount of

1,4-*cis*- and *trans*-units. It was mentioned, that use of vanadium catalysts without chlorine atoms (on the base of $V(AcAc)_3$ or $V(OBu)_4$ with $Al(Et)_3$) also leads to the opening of cycles in cyclobutene or in its 3-methylderivative [38].

Polymers producing from cyclobutene with the help of titanium Ziegler catalytic systems have different chemical and spatial structure in dependence on catalyst type and polymerization conditions. So, on $Al(Et)_3$–$TiCl_4$ at Al : Ti = 3 and −50°C in *n*-heptane 1,4-*cis*-PB is predominantly formed [36], and in toluene at Al : Ti = 2 and −10°C polymer with prevail content of 1,4-*trans*-units is formed [37]. Conversion of monomer into polymer occurs quantitatively.

There are some other catalysts on the base of halogenides of VIII group elements (Ru, Ir, Os) that polymerize cycloolefines with high tension energy of the ring in polar mediums [39]. Thus, in the work [40] it was shown that $RhCl_3 \cdot 3H_2O$ in ethanol converts cyclobutene into 1,4-*trans*-PB, and 3-methylcyclobutene into completely 1,4-*trans*-PPD.

Chemical analogues of PB, including those with predominant content of *trans*-units can be produced also by opening the rings with biggest sizes than of cyclobutene. For example, with the help of Ziegler systems on the base of WCl_6 polymerization of cyclic di- and trienes with opening of the rings was carried out [41]. $Al(i\text{-}Bu)_3$, $Al(i\text{-}Bu)_2H$, $AlEtCl_2$, *n*-BuLi were used as cocatalysts. Polymers from 1,5-cyclooctadiene and 1,5,9-cyclododecatriene, so-called polybutenamers, on their merits have the structure of 1,4-polymers of butadiene, but are differ by absence of side groups [42, 43].

Polymerization reactions of not tension cycloolefines with opening of the ring are very spesific, especially in the case of three-component Ziegler systems on the base of W. Analogues reactions of high tension cycles significantly less spesific. Thus, complexes of Mo or W salts with organoaluminum compounds (OAC) initiate the formation from cyclobutene as 1,4-butadiene (containing equimolar amounts of 1,4-*cis*- and 1,4-*trans*-units), so cyclobutane fragments in polymer that testifies to stereospecificity absence [37]. Under catalysis on π–allyl complexes of W one is succeeded in direct of cyclobutene polymerization to predominant formation of 1,4-*cis*- and 1,4-*trans*-PB [44].

Two- and three-component Ziegler-Natta catalysts on the base of Ta for cyclodienes and cyclotrienes polymerization are suggested in [45]. So, in the presence of $TaCl_5$–$AlEtCl_2$ with or without additions of oxygen-containing activators (alcohols, ketones, epoxides) 1,5-cyclooctadiene and 1,5,9-cyclo-dodeca-triene are practically completely converted into *trans*-polyalkenomeres. Interest-ing data are presented in work [46], where from 1-methyl(ethyl) -, 1,2-dimethyl, and 1-chloro-1,5-cyclooctadiene on WCl_6–EtOH–$AlEtCl_2$ system completely alternative copolymers of butadiene and its derivatives were synthesized.

All polymers produced by the opening of rings of 3-substituted cycloolefines, even completely stereoregulative in relation to double bond are amorphous and apparently atactive. In other words, either catalysts don't display stereoselectivity in relation to one in a two monomer antipodes, or stereoselectivity is broken as a consequence of racemation in polymerization process.

ZIEGLER-NATTA CATALYSTS TITANIUM CATALYSTS

In the case of titanium catalytic systems stereoregularity of forming polydienes depends on molar ratio of components, nature of groups connecting with titanium (Cl, Br, I, OR), valence state and allotrope modification of transition metal compound, organometallic compound nature, various additives [47, 48]. Some Ziegler titanium catalysts of dienes *trans*-polymerization are presented in table 2. Stereospecificity of $TiCl_4$–AlR_3 catalyst is determined by ratio of its components. So, at Al : Ti = 1 PB with mixed microstructure is formed (55-60% of 1,4-*cis*- and 35-40% of 1,4-*trans*-units). With twofold and more excess of AlR_3 the complex becomes *trans*-regulating as for butadiene [49], so for isoprene [50] polymerizations. Variation of stereospecificity is associated with the fact that transition metal in active sites may be in different valent states and contains those or another groups at reaction center.

Titanium active sites stereospecificity is also changed when varying allotrope modification of transition metal compound (α-, β-, γ-, δ-$TiCl_3$) [51-53]. Thus, β-$TiCl_3$ in combination with various OAC is high stereospecific *cis*-regu-lating catalyst for isoprene polymerization. In the case of PB synthesis on the same complexes polymer microstructure significantly depends on aluminum-al-kyl nature [51, 54]. On β-$TiCl_3$–$Al(Et)_3$ system amorphous PB with mixed microstructure (37% of *cis*- and 60% of *trans*-units) was received [51], the use of $AlEtCl_2$ leads to formation of PB with 99% of 1,4-*trans*-units [54].

Titanium systems of *trans*-polymerization of pentadiene are not numerous: so, from *trans*-pentadiene under the action of γ–$TiCl_3$·0,33$AlCl_3$ catalyst polymer with predominant content of 1,4-*trans*-units in the chain (up to 88%) is formed, the rest are 1,2-structures [63]. It is interesting that *cis*-regulating complex TiI_4–AlR_3 for polymerization of butadiene and isoprene becomes *trans*-regulating under pentadiene polymerization [49].

Analysis of table 2 data testifies to the fact that titanium catalysts initiating *trans*-polymerization of dienes contain halogen (in the majority of cases chlorine) as a one or another component. Under butadiene polymerization on the $Ti(OR')_4$–$AlRCl_2$ system its stereospecificity of action is determined by the ratio Al : Ti, monomer and solvent nature, nature of radical at titanium atom. So, complex $Ti(OBu)_4$–$AlEtCl_2$ (Al : Ti = 10) forms crystal 1,4-*trans*-PB, whereas in the same conditions polyisoprene containing only 38% of 1,4-*trans*-units was obtained. When Al : Ti ratio decreases down to 4–6 noticed system becomes *cis*-regulating in relation to isoprene and forms PB with mixed microstructure [49, 64]. Radical structure at transition metal and nature of using solvent are of significant importance.

Titanium tetraalkoxides with primary radicals of as linear, so branched structure independently on solvent nature form *cis*-regulating catalysts, whereas titanates with tertiary radicals lead to the formation of *trans*-polyisoprene. Titanium tetraalkoxides with secondary radicals in aliphatic solvents give 1,4-*cis*-, and in aromatic hydrocarbons – 1,4-*trans*-polyisoprene. In dependence on type of used solvent and titanate structure either α–, or β–crystal modification of $TiCl_3$ is formed, and it determines stereospecificity of total system [62].

The influence of additions of various nature on stereospecificity of titani-um systems are not simple. Introduction of bases (amines, pyridines) into $Ti(AcAc)_3$ –$Al(Et)_2Cl$ complex leads to the increase of 1,4-*trans*-units content in PB mainly at the expense of 1,4-*cis*-units

[65]. Analogous effect is observed under addition of ethers, thioethers, tertiary amines into TiI_4–AlR_3 catalyst [66-69].

Introduction of dimethyl ether into $TiCl_4$–I_2–$Al(Et)_2H$–(*n*-Bu)Li complex converts it into *trans*-regulating, and with the increase of ether quantity 1,4-*trans*-units content in PB is rises [70]. According to degree of influence on microstructure ethers are arranged in row: dimethyl > methylethyl > diethyl > > dibutyl. In other words, their influence reduces with hydrocarbon radicals length increase, that coincides with decrease of addiction to complex formation [67]. Tendency of 1,4-*trans*-units amount increase in PB under addition of amines was also noted on $TiCl_4$–AlR_3 system, that without amines gave polymer of mixed structure [71]. The addition of tetrahydrothiofuran into *cis*-regulating systems $TiCl_3$–$3AlI_3$–AlR_3 [71], $TiCl_4$–I_2–$Al(Et)_3$ [72] leads to formation of PB with 1,4-*trans*-units content from 65 to 88%, instead of 87% of 1,4-*cis*-units.

Under the use of organomagnesium compounds as cocatalyst (MgR_2, RMgCl) in combination with $TiCl_4$forming systems display nearly equal stereospecificity under as butadiene [73], so isoprene [74] polymerization (1,4-*trans*-units content is 60-80%). Substitution of MgR_2 by cocatalyst containing iodine in its structure (RMgI + R_2Mg) increases complex stereospecificity under 1,4-*trans*-polymerization of isoprene, but reduces under butadiene polymerization (1,4-*trans*-units contents are 98 and 42% in PI and PB accordingly) [75].

Analysis of literature data shows that titanium Ziegler systems are not perspective for *trans*-polymerization of as butadiene, so other dienes because of their stereospecificity and activity. The situation was changed a little with the beginning of application of catalysts supports that proved to be good under olefines polymerization. In works [76, 77] *trans*-polymerization of butadiene and isoprene on silica gel supported titanium-magnesium catalysts (TMC) in combination with Al(*i*-Bu)$_3$ was investigated. TMC modificated by organometallic zirconium compounds also lead to *trans*-PB formation [78, 83] (table 3). Polymerization rate and microstructure of forming polymers are determined by molar ratio Al : Ti in catalytic system and polymerization temperature [76]. 1,4-*Transi*-units content in polydienes in dependence on polymerization conditions is 81,5-94%. It is suggested that supports of $MgCl_2$ type play dual role: they increase active surface of heterogeneous catalyst and forward to formation of active $TiCl_3$ in necessary for diene *trans*-polymerization α–, δ– or γ–modification [84].

Thus, in spite of variety of stereospecific in relation to 1,4-*trans*-polydienes formation, including PB, titanium systems (table 2 and 3) the set of forming active sites types significantly less; they contain, presumably violet (α–, γ–, δ–) modification of $TiCl_3$ in combination with cocatalyst [47, 48, 85].

Vanadium Catalysts

Among catalysts for diene *trans*-polymerization systems on the base of vanadium compounds are described in literature more particular. They display good *trans*-regulating ability and high activity with the use of activating methods. So, vanadium halogenides in combination with aluminum alkyls independently from using diene nature (butadiene, isoprene, pentadiene) are specific catalysts for synthesis of polydienes with high content of

1,4-*trans*-units (table 4). Stereospecificity of chlorine containing vanadium compounds under as isoprene [52, 86], so butadiene [87, 88] polymerization reduces in row VCl_3–VCl_4–$VOCl_3$ when vanadium valence rises. The highest *trans*-units content is achieved under the action of VCl_3–$Al(Et)_3$ catalyst. Substitution of one or two chlorine atoms by alcohol or carboxyl groups, AlR_3 by AlR_2Cl doesn't lead to significant change in polymer microstructure. 1,4-*Trans*-units content in polydienes is also slightly depends on ratio of catalytic system components and polymerization temperature.

Activity of vanadium compounds under butadiene and isoprene polymerization is changed in row: $VCl_4 > VOCl_3 > VCl_3$ [86, 88]. For acceleration of dienes polymerization on vanadium systems they use supported catalysts [96], activating promoters, mainly electron-donor compounds (ethers, amines, sulfides, phosphanes) [98] or additions of other transition metal compounds [54].

On heterogeneous system VCl_3–$AlEt_3$ highmolecular polymers of butadiene, isoprene and pentadiene with high crystalline degree and of predominantly 1,4-*trans*-structure (up to 99%) are formed [87]. The polymer yield on such systems is not big but it can be increase by formation of the catalyst on support in fine-dispersion state, for example: VCl_3 on such inactive supports as kaolin or titanium dioxide [96]. Attempts to increase VCl_3–$Al(Et)_3$ complex activity by its modification with the help of various electron-donor compounds were undertaken. It was shown that additions of strong electron-donors such as triethylamine and pyridine inhibited polymerization. Introduction of a weak donor – diisopropyl ether – increases catalyst activity in 5-10 times without polymer microstructure change [98-100].

The use of VCl_4 allows to achieve more high dienes polymerization rates. However polymerization of, for example, isoprene on VCl_4–AlR_3 system has non-stationary character [86, 101], apparently because of the active sites deactivation (quick vanadium reduction to inactive valence state). They can be stabilized by the use of inert support (TiO_2, Al_2O_3, etc.) for VCl_4 or by portion introduction of organoaluminum cocatalyst in two stages with intermediate thermal treatment [102, 103].

Significant influence of OAC nature and concentration on process character is characteristic for catalytic systems on the base of $VOCl_3$. So, for butadiene polymerization on $VOCl_3$–$Al(Et)_3$ system maximum process rate was observed at ratio Al : V = 2–3. Under substitution of $Al(Et)_3$ by weak alkylating $Al(Et)_2Cl$ catalyst activity monotonously increases with components ratio rise. Microstructure of received on these systems PB is not sensitive to the change of ratio Al : V [88]. It is interesting that optimum of activity on one and the same catalyst depends on monomer nature. So, under isoprene polymerization on $VOCl_3$–$Al(Et)_3$ system maximum process rate achieves at ratio Al : V = 1 [97, 104]. It was shown in work [105] that under isoprene polymerization on $VOCl_3$–$Al(i\text{-}Bu)_3$ complex two activity maximums are observed: at Al : V = 0,3 and 1,5. the first one is associated with cationic polymerization, and the second one – with ion-coordinating polymerization. With ratio rise from 1 up to 4 1,4-*trans*-units content increase from 60 to 90%.

Authors of [106, 107] were succeeded in homogenization of VCl_3–AlR_3 system by introduction of three tetrahydrophurane (THP) molecules that allows to increase the rate of polymerization of butadiene and pentadiene significantly, and insignificantly of isoprene polymerization. Homogenous vanadium catalysts consisting of mixture of $VCl_3 \cdot 3THP$ or $V(AcAc)_3$ with $Al(Et)_2Cl$ polymerize only *trans*-isomer of pentadiene [106]. Amorphous products containing 60 and 40% of 1,4-*trans*- and 1,2-*trans*-units accordingly are formed [101].

At the same time in work [107] it was established that under the influence of homogenous catalyst $VCl_3 \cdot 3THP–Al(i\text{-}Bu)_3$ (in contrast to mentioned above) the both pentadiene isomers participate in stereospecific *trans*-polymerization and they polymerize with nearly equal rates. Polymers obtained from *trans*-pentadiene contain 68% of 1,4-*trans*- and 32% of 1,2-*trans*-units. From *cis*-pentadiene PPD consisting of predominantly 1,4-*trans*-structures (up to 97%) and 3–5% of 1,2-units is formed.

Catalysts on the base of three- and four-valent vanadium can be homogenized by complete or partial substitution of vanadium environment by chelate or carboxyl groups. So, under polymerization of butadiene on $V(C_7H_{15}COO)Cl_3–Al(Et)_3$ or $V(AcAc)_3–Al(Et)_2Cl$ complexes polymer with 90 and 100% of 1,4-*trans*-units accordingly can be received [108]. However, if instead of $Al(Et)_2Cl$ one will use $Al(Et)_3$ polymer with 90% of 1,2-units is formed [164], as in the case $V(NETt_4–Al(Et)_3$ [109].

It is obvious out of given above examples that catalytic systems containing chlorine atom either in vanadium environment, or at aluminum atom form 1,4-*trans*-polydienes. In the absence of halogen 1,2-structures are formed. Situation is significantly changed if we use aluminoxanes as the second component. So, under butadiene polymerization on $V(AcAc)_3$–methylalumoxane (MAO) at Al : V = 10 and 30 polymers containing accordingly 87 [110] and 90% of *trans*-1,4 units [111, 112] are formed. The rise of Al : V ratio up to 1000 leads to the increase of 1,4-*trans*-units content up to 100% [113]. In spite of such big amounts of MAO its total concentration is not high because of low content of $V(AcAc)_3$ – $1 \cdot 10^{-4}$ mole / l. Butadiene conversion is 47% for 15 min at 15°C. Polymer is characterized by high molecular mass ([η] = 3,2 dl / g). In other words this system has working characteristics that are enough acceptable for industry application.

But the use of another vanadium derivative with less polarity substituents ($V(t\text{-}OBu)_4$) in combination with MAO leads to formation of PB containing approximately equal amounts of 1,2- and 1,4-*cis*-structures, and PI with 1,2- (up to 30%) and 3,4-units [110]. The use of cyclopentadienyl vanadium compounds ($CpVCl_2 \cdot (P(Et)_3)_2$ or Cp_2VCl) in combination with MAO in contrast to another vanadium catalysts containing in their ligand environment chlorine atoms leads to the formation of PB with predominant content of 1,4-*cis*-units (up to 90%) [113].

Monomer nature and polymerization conditions also influence on polymers microstructure. Butadiene and *cis*-isomer of pentadiene in the presence of $V(AcAc)_3$–MAO give 1,4-*trans*-polymers as at low, so at room temperature. Isoprene, 2-ethylbutadiene-1,3 and *trans*-2-methylpentadiene-1,3 at low temperature (lower than –20°C) form predominantly 1,4-*trans*-polymers, and at room temperature – of mixed *cis*/*trans*-structures [112].

Ion-Coordinating Catalysts on the Base of Other Transition Metals

Catalysts of Ziegler type or individual organic compounds on the base of another than V or Ti transition metals (Cr, Fe, Co, Ni, Rh), including lanthanides can initiate *trans*-polymerization of dienes.

Data on iron-containing catalysts are not numerous and are not of great interest because of low yields and stereoregularity of polymer. Synthesis of PB containing 73% of 1,4-*trans*-units and 31% of gel in the presence of $Fe(C_7H_{15}COO)_3$–$AlEt)_3$ complex with 2-mercaptobenzimidazole additives is mentioned [114]. On the same catalytic system but with dodecyldithiooxamide addition PPD with 54% of 1,4-*trans*-units is formed [115]. Under the introduction into complex of butylthiocyanate the received polymer contains only 4% of 1,4-*trans*-units, but up to 81% of 1,2-*trans*-units with syndiotactic position of side chains [116].

Under butadiene polymerization on cobalt catalysts of Ziegler type on the base of soluble in hydrocarbons Co compounds (acetylacetonates, octanates, naphtanes) with *n*-alkylphenyl (diphenyl) addition one will be succeeded in formation of PB with 1,4-*trans*-structures content up to 75-85%, high crystalline degree and low gel content [117]. For inhibition of gel-formation CS_2 is added to the system. *Trans*-PB with controlled molecular mass can be synthesized in the presence of such electron-donor compounds as dialkyl-, diarylsulfoxides [118]. Stereospecificity of action of nickel-containing compounds of general formula π–R_nNiX (R – alkyl, crotyl, pentenyl; X – halogen, CCl_3COO, CF_3COO etc.) is determined mainly by the nature of acid residue connecting with nickel atom [1]. So, π–allyl(crotyl)nickeliodide(bromide) and bis–π–alkenylnickeliodide (bromide) are the catalysts leading to the formation of butadiene and isoprene crystalline *trans*-polymers [119, 120]. Nickel-containing catalysts without organoaluminum component and consisting of π–allylnickeltriflourineacetate in dependence on nature of solvent and addition ligands may form PB with high 1,4-*cis*-units content (up to 88-92% in heptane), equibinar (in benzene) or *trans*-PB (96-98% of 1,4-*trans*-units) in benzene with $P(OPh)_3$ additives [121]. Catalytic activity and selectivity of complexes of general formula (η3–$C_3H_5NiL)PF_6$ under butadiene polymerization depend on electron and steric characteristics of ligand L [122]. Complex with $L = P(OET)_3$ forms PB with 1,4-*trans*-units content 85-90% in methanol, acetonitryl, benzene, THP or cyclohexane only at 80°C. In the case of $L = P(i\text{-}OPr)_3$ polymerization occurs even at 25°C, polymer contains up to 98% of 1,4-*trans*-units. In dependence of using solvent activity changes in row: benzene > chloroform ≈ THP > cyclohexane ≈ acetone >> methanol > acetonitryl. In work [123] synthesis of 1,4-*trans*-PB with high crystalline degree on catalytic system containing compounds of carboxylating nickeloxyborates of formula $(RCOONiO)_3B$ and $(RCOONiO)_2BOR$ (R – alkyl-, aryl-, alkylaryl-, alcoxygroup), organophosphorus compounds of formula $(ArO_3)P$ and carbon or fluorinecarbon acids was described.

All known cobalt- and nickel-containing catalysts are of low activity. As it follows from data given above for their *trans*-stereospecificity display there are some requirements to the reaction medium components. Practically in all cases polymers with low molecular mass are formed because of high rate of chain transfer on monomer [124].

There are no enough data on application of zirconium catalysts for diene *trans*-polymerization. In patent [125] they reported about reception of 1,4-*trans*-PB on $ZrCl_4$–$Al(i\text{-}Bu)_3$ system with high stereospecificity of action only in the case of careful purification of zirconium chloride from $FeCl_3$ impurities. In other case polymer of mixed microstructure is formed.

Systems on the base of Rh, Pd, Ir compounds initiating stereospecificity *trans*-polymerization of dienes in polar mediums present an interesting group of catalysts [126, 127]. Rhodium complexes of Ziegler type are mainly of scientific interest because of low yield and molecular mass of PB and PI, although 1,4-*trans*-units content in them is 93%. For example, the yield of PB with *trans*-units content 92,2% and [η] up to 0,61 dl / g for 24 hours at 40°C on $Rh(CO)_4$–$Al(Et)_3$–$AlCl_3$ complex in benzene is 11,2% [128]. Molecular mass of 1,4-*trans*-PB received in the presence of allyl or crotyl complex of Rh in combination with $Al(Et)_2Cl$ doesn't exceed 2000. by this ligand nature influences only on activity, but not stereospecificity of catalyst action [128].

It must be noted that 1,4-*trans*-polymerization of dienes occurs in the pre-sence of chrom-oxide catalysts also. It is suggested [1] that π–allyl compound of chromium formed as a result of interaction between activated metal and monomer is the active site of polymerization. Polymerization on these catalysts occurs by mechanism of "live" chains. One of the limitations of noted systems are reduced physico-chemical properties of isoprene polymers presumably because of some destructions of "head-to-tail" connections in structure of the last ones.

Polymers of mixed structure and low molecular mass were received under isoprene and butadiene polymerization on *tris*–π–allylchromium [129]. The same situation is observed under PPD synthesis, but *trans*-monomer polymerizes quicker than *cis*-pentadiene which most likely slowly isomerizes into *trans*-form [130]. However, if they use of aluminumsilicate as a support for $(\pi\text{–}C_3H_5)_3Cr$ stereospecificity of system action sharply changes: crystalline 1,4-*trans*-polydienes are formed [129, 131].

In present times this system is the only one competitive catalyst with compounds on the base of vanadium and titanium for activity and formed *trans*-polydienes properties. The limitations of chromium-oxide catalysts are many stages and technology complication of their reception. PB with high 1,4-*trans*-units content can de synthesized by adding a little amount of oxygen to π–allyl chromium derivatives [132].

Lanthanide and actinide catalysts are differ from other Ziegler systems by their ability to polymerize dienes with 1,4-connection of units mainly of *cis*-configuration. But there are some examples of 1,4-*trans*-polydienes synthesis with the use of f-elements, first of all lanthanides.

The distinctive feature of the majority of *trans*-regulating lanthanide catalysts is the absence of halogenides in their structure. Thus, polydienes with predominant content of 1,4-*trans*-structures are formed in the presence of organic compounds of lanthanides: neodymium isopropylate, benzoate or carboxy-late in combination with AlR_3 [133], MgR_2 [134, 135] or RLi [136], tribenylneo-dymium etherate [137], *tris*-(oligodienyl)lanthanide [138], organometallic deri-vatives of $(\pi\text{–}C_3H_5)_4LiLn$ type [139] including those on the base of Sm. Complexes $[(CpR)_2Sm(\pi\text{–}C_3H_5)]_n$ and $(CpR)_2Sm(\pi\text{–}C_3H_5)L$ ($R = CH(CH_3)_2$, L = THP or $Li(\pi\text{–}C_3H_5)$) polymerize isoprene without aluminum cocatalyst. Polymerization is highly stereospecific and leads to the quantitative formation of 1,4-*trans*-PI [140]. It is known that catalysts containing halogenides of Eu and Sm are inactive in *cis*-polymerization of dienes because they reduce to inactive two-valent state under action of cocatalysts – OAC [141]. At the same time in work [142] possibility of *trans*-PB formation on $Nd(Pr)Cl_2{\cdot}nTHP$ complexes and without additive alkylating agents was noted. Moreover addition of AlR_3 converts these system into *cis*-regulating [142].

Under diene polymerization on tribenzylneodymium it was established that in initiating reaction all three bonds C–Nd participate and active site represents polymer analogue of *tris*-(crotyl)isoprenylneodymium [143].

The presence of halogenides in lanthanide catalysts structure doesn't prevent their *trans*-stereospecificity of action. The last is displayed under polymerization on lanthanide–aluminum systems in the case of further complicating of monomer structure: for example, from *trans*-pentadiene-1,3, *trans*-2-methylpentadiene-1,3 and *trans*, *trans*-hexadiene-2,4 polymers are formed containing 3-5, 60 and 98% of 1,4-*trans*-units, accordingly [144, 145]. At thc same time substitution of OAC by organomagnesium cocatalyst leads to complete inversion of *cis*-stereospecificity of complex on the base of neodymium chloride under butadiene polymerization [146] and to the formation of *trans*-PB. It is suggested that Grin'yar reagent in contrast to OAC completely alkylates neodymium chloride and forms *trans*-regulating trialkylneodymium.

It must be noted, that active sites of neodecanoate neodymium complex in combination with Bu_2Mg under butadiene polymerization are haloginated in the case of introduction of $Al_2Et_3Cl_3$ into reaction medium. Further propagation of "living" chain continue at the expense of connection of units with 1,4-*cis*-structure. The so-called "block-copolymer" is formed which is differ from mixture of *cis*- and *trans*-PB and exhibits itself as thermoelastoplast with melting temperature 140–150°C [134].

CATALYSTS ON THE BASE OF TWO TRANSITION METALS

Ziegler-Natta catalysts consisting of two or more transition metals one of which usually vanadium or titanium are very perspective for 1,4-*trans*-poly-merization of dienes. The majority of investigations were directed on *trans*-poly-merization of isoprene in the presence of mixed catalysts. There are few analogous data on synthesis of *trans*-PB (table 5) and *trans*-PPD [147], however general situation is identical for all dienes. So, joint sedimentation of VCl_3 with $TiCl_3$ [54], $Ti(OR)_4$ [96] leads to significant increase of isoprene polymerization rate without reduce of 1,4-*trans*-units content. About high activity of such mixed catalysts is said in [148] where for reception of crystalline 1,4-*trans*-polydienes the following mixtures were used: $VOCl_3$ or VCl_4 with$TiCl_4$; $TiCl_4$ with $CoCl_2$ or $FeCl_3$. When introduce $CoCl_2$ (Co : Ti = 2,3) into $TiCl_4$–$Al(Et)_3$ complex the last one becomes active 1,4-*trans*-regulating under isoprene polymerization, whereas without cobalt halogenides oligomer products are formed mainly [149]. Analogous stereospecificity change proceeds after addition to $TiOR_4$ ($TiCl_4$)–AlR_3 system of ferri-compound, by this polydienes with 1,4-*trans*-units content up to 97-100% are formed [150]. Authors of [151] noticed that on $Ni(C_7H_{15}COO)_2$–$TiCl_4$–$Al(Et)_3$ complex predominantly 1,4-*trans*-PI is formed.

Activity of VCl_4–$Al(i\text{-}Bu)_3$ significantly increases under $TiCl_4$ addition [152-157], polymerization proceeds with stationary rate until complete expense of monomer. It is interesting to note that molecular mass of 1,4-*trans*-PI increases with the rise of ratio Al : (Ti + V) [157].

In work [164] they observed sharp increase of activity of VCl_3–$Al(i\text{-}Bu)_3$ catalyst under isoprene polymerization when increase the time of collective thermal treatment of mixture α–$TiCl_3$–VCl_3 in comparison with VCl_3–$Al(i\text{-}Bu)_3$ and α–$TiCl_3$–$Al(i\text{-}Bu)_3$ systems that were subjected to thermal treatment separately. In all cases *trans*-stereospecificity remains constant (96-98%). It is reported about significant increase of activity of VCl_4–$TiCl_4$(γ–$TiCl_3$)–AlR_3 system when using the method of AlR_3 introduction in two portions with intermediate thermal treatment [147, 152, 157, 165]. It is suggested that it associated with the increase of specific surface of VCl_3, that occurs as a result of insertion of vanadium chloride on highly dispersion $TiCl_3$ that plays the role of inert support and doesn't participate in polymerization, during thermal treatment [54]. At the same time in works [164, 166, 167] on the base of investigation of influence of α–$TiCl_3$, $FeCl_3$, WCl_6, Ti(*n*-OBu)$_3$ and $ZrCl_4$ additives on activity and stereospecificity of action of vanadium and titanium catalysts under isoprene polymerization they made the assumption that their high activity is associated with the formation during thermal treatment of transition metals double chlorides.

Addition of small amounts of titanium compounds (up to 10 mole % to V) to the $VOCl_3$–Al(*i*-Bu)$_3$ system leads to noticeable rise of catalyst activity in the case of isoprene polymerization and at low temperatures, and with maintenance of constant 1,4-*trans*-units content in polymer. Efficiency of additions decreases in row Ti(*n*-OBu)Cl_3 – $TiCl_4$ – Ti(*n*-OBu)$_4$ [168]. Effect of activity rise under mixing of several transition metals derivatives is also observed for homogenous systems, for example VCl_3–Ti(OR)$_4$–Al(Et)$_3$ [96]. Complex responsible for stereospecificity control of *trans*-polymerization is formed as a result of reaction between VCl_3 and Al(Et)$_3$. Simultaneously the reduction of Ti(OR)$_4$ by triethylaluminum to unstable titanium ethylalcoholates that transfer heterogeneous complex VCl_3–Al(Et)$_3$ to homogeneous state occurs, and this increases polydiene yield. However, homogeneity of the system is not satisfactory condition for activity increase. Authors of [96] consider that active sites of polymerization consist of compounds of all three metals, i.e. new type of active sites is formed, so, not only physical state of catalyst changes. Molecular mass increase under addition of titanium alcoholate to VCl_3–Al(Et)$_3$ complex is also testifies to it. Polydienes molecular mass increase on catalysts on the base of two transition metals is also reported in works [152, 154, 165, 169].

For identification of reasons of high activity of systems with two transition metals formation of metals double chlorides was investigated in works [170-173]. In dependence on components ratio complexes $CrTi_3Cl_{12}$, $MoTi_3Cl_{12}$, $NiTi_2Cl_8$, $FeTi_2Cl_8$, $VTi_{1,1}Cl_{6,6}$ and other were received. Practically in all cases $TiCl_3$ was in α– or γ–modification. Presumably compounds of the second metal of variable valence promote transformation of β–$TiCl_3$ into violet modification at temperature lower than 170°C. Authors of [170] make a conclusion that one of the conditions for double salts formation is isomorphism of their chloride crystals that enter to the interaction.

Thus, the meaning of additions activating influence is in insertion of one transition metal compound upon another one [54]; stabilization of active sites by the second metal compound, formed from organic derivative of vanadium [86, 96, 157]; homogenization of catalytic system [96]; change of active sites structure by the formation of double chlorides on account of proximity of parameters of individual chlorides lattices [174].

In works [175, 176] high active and *trans*-stereospecific mixed vanadium-titanium catalysts for polymerization of isoprene and isomers of pentadiene allowing to synthesize high molecular polymers are suggested; they are successfully used in industrial production of 1,4-*trans*-PI (synthetic gutta-percha).

OTHER 1,4-*TRANS*-POLYDIENES

There are a few data on reception of *trans*-polymers from substituted conjugated 1,3-dienes. Polymer from 2-ethylbutadiene with high content of 1,4-*trans*-units is synthesized with the help of the same catalysts that for synthetic gutta-percha reception, but with lower rates, for example on VCl_3–$Al(Et)_3$ (Al : V = 3,5). Polydiene has low melting temperature (42°C) probable because of the volumetric ethyl side groups [177]. At the same time 2,3-dimethyl-butadiene under its polymerization in heptane on $TiCl_4$–Al(*i*-Bu)$_3$ (Al : Ti = 1 : 4) forms product with melting temperature 253-259°C and $[\eta] = 0{,}5\text{-}1{,}3$ dl / g [178]. Introduction into isoprene instead of methyl more volumetric groups, for example phenyl or 2-tretbutyl leads to S-*cis*-conformation of double bonds in monomer and as a result only 1,4-*cis*-polymers are formed [179].

In the case of 2-methylpentadiene the rate of *trans*-polymerization in comparison with pentadiene-1,3 is significantly lower. Thus, on Ti(O-Bu)$_4$ –VCl_3–Al(*i*-Bu)$_3$ complex (Ti : V : Al = 1 : 2 : 20) monomer conversion for 26 days at room temperature is 50% [180]. Polymer practically consists of 1,4-*trans*-units with two melting temperatures (182 and 192°C). Catalyst $CoCl_2$–$Al(Et)_2Cl$–thiophene (thiophene : Al : Co = 200 : 200 : 1, benzene, 0°C) gives amorphous polymer with 1,4-*trans*-units content 94%, analogously to complexes VCl_3 or $VOCl_3$ with $Al(Et)_3$.

Vanadium catalyst VCl_3–Al(*i*-Bu)$_3$ (Al : V = 5,8) is able to polymerize conjugated diene – α–myrcene (2-methyl-6-methylene-1,7-octadiene) with formation of stiff polymers with high molecular mass; these polymers contain some amount of gel probably because of the participation of double bonds of side substituents in crosslinking reactions [181]. All these polymerization examples and forming products are of scientific interest only yet.

PROPERTIES AND APPLICATION FIELDS OF 1,4-*TRANS*-POLYDIENES

1,4-*Trans*-PB forms crystals with pseudo-hexagonale element cells; the configuration of chain is zigzag; it is the only one polydiene containing mesophases approximating by their structure to liquid crystals [182]. It has two melting temperature intervals 50-70°C and 135-155°C [183] because it exists in two enanthiotropic crystalline modifications. In spite of this polymer has very low glass transition temperature (–90°C) and this positive fact can be practically realized when one succeeded in PB crystallinity decrease (by vulcanization, copolymerization etc.). PB strength, solidity, elasticity increase with the rise of 1,4-*trans*-units content and its molecular mass. By its solidity and elasticity at room temperature PB is close to 1,4-*trans*-PI but acquiesce in strength. Crystalline degree of PB with 99% of 1,4-*trans*-units achieves 70-80%. The crystalline degree reduces with decrease of *trans*-units content, temperature rise and increase of vulcanization degree. Crystallinity of polymer with 65-75% of 1,4-*trans*-units is not significant and completely disappears after vulcanization. Thermodynamic pliability of *trans*-PB macromolecules is close to pliability of 1,4-*trans*-PI chains and higher than of PB 1,4-*cis*-isomers [184].

Vulcanizates of homo-1,4-*trans*-PB are differ by high modules, strength and wear-resistance. By wear-resistance they are far and away from vulcanizates of natural and butadiene–styrene rubbers; by strength and elasticity they are close to butadiene–styrene rubber vulcanizates. Polymer is interesting for foot rubbers production, floor coverings, insertions and other technical wares (for which high wear-resistance in combination with solidity and good strength properties is necessary). Out of mixture of natural and butadiene–styrene rubbers together with *trans*-PB they recommended to produce tire rubbers [185].

Compositions on the base of *trans*-PB posses also good electro-isolation properties; they are used for capsulation of electric transformers [186], for isolation of electrical cables [187].

Synthetic gutta-percha or 1,4-*trans*-PI is a crystalline plastic, that differ from nature analogues by its high purity, less regular structure (content of *trans*-units is 93-99%), more high molecular mass and somewhat higher branching. It is also exists in three polymorphous crystalline modifications: α (arising only in intense polymer), β and γ (period of identity is 4,7 and 8,8Å, melting temperature interval is 55-54 and 64-74°C accordingly).

Polymer characterized by high ozone-resistance, resistance to HF and HCl action, to action of alkalis, greases and oils, by extraordinary less water-absorption. Vulcanization at temperatures lower than melting temperature of crystalline formations of 1,4-*trans*-PI gives vulcanizates with properties characteristic to crystalline polymers (high modules, solidity, etc.). High-temperature vulcanization leads to the formation of soft rubbers. As in the case of natural rubber introduction of active extenders slightly influences on strength at tension, decreases elasticity and increases wear-resistance, solidity, vulcanizates modulesand resistance to disruption.

Vulcanizates of synthetic gutta-percha have high mechanical properties, resistant to abrasion, multiple deformations. By two last parameters they exceed vulcanizates of natural rubber. 1,4-*trans*-PI connects well with all rubbers, polyolefines, polyamides [188]. All these properties condition the possibility of application of synthetic gutta-percha for isolation of submarine and underground cables, for production of straps and transport belts. Polymer is used as adhesive insertion for doubling of heat-, vibro- and sound-isolation materials. There are examples of synthetic gutta-percha application in chemical engineering, for production of sport inventory and other ware of special meaning [189]. Application of synthetic gutta-percha as additions increasing cohesion strength of crude rubber mixtures in production of tires is admitted as perspective [190].

In work [191] expedience of introduction of synthetic gutta-percha into compositions with natural, butadiene or butadiene–styrene rubbers was shown. Vulcanizates of such mixtures have excellent dynamic mechanical properties, high modules, wear-resistance and resistance to abrasion. Authors of patent [192] suggests to use in tire production more complicated compositions, including1,4-*cis*-PI, 1,4-*trans*-PB (instead of synthetic gutta-percha) and 3,4-PI.

High adhesion of synthetic gutta-percha to metals and leather and other materials allows to use polymer in various adhesive compositions [193]. 1,4-*Trans*-PI possesses all properties that are necessary for its application in orthopedy and regenerating surgery (thermoplasticity, strength, high rigidity, ability to keep necessary form) [194]. Polymer should contain not less than 85% of 1,4-*trans*-units, molecular mass equal $85\text{-}200 \cdot 10^3$ and 20-40% of crystalline phase [195, 196]. The possibility of application of foam synthetic gutta-percha [197].

1,4-*Trans*-PPD received on modificated vanadium-titanium catalysts of Ziegler type has $M = (5\text{-}7) \cdot 10^5$, glass transition temperature –50°C and melting temperature 80°C. Tests showed that rubbers mixtures on its base have high values of cohesion strength [169]. Good film-formation properties and adhesion to frame polyvinyl films allow to recommend highmolecular 1,4-*trans*-PPD as adhesion covering in production of footwear thermoplastic materials [169].

Pentadiene oligomers with predominant content of 1,4-*trans*-units received by cationic polymerization are interesting as raw materials for a lot of products synthesis. They are readily subjected to oxidative polymerization via double bonds that allows to use them as substitutes of natural oils. So, for production of boiled linseed oil and other lacquer-dyeing materials pentadiene oligomers synthesized in the presence of $TiCl_4$ [198], P_2O_5 [199], Al(*i*-Bu)$_3$ [200] are used. Oligopentadiene received under the action of CH_3COOH is recommended as base of quickly dry lacquers and additives [25].

All *trans*-polydienes are thermoplastic materials. But there are some exeptions, for example elastomeric polychloroprene (PCP), containing units of mainly *trans*-configuration. Chloroprene rubber possesses number of important properties: high plasticity, good elasticity, etc. The most important specific properties of rubbers from PCP are oil-, benzene-, ozone-, light-, heat- and fire-resistance, good adhesion to some substrates, low gas-penetration. Due to these properties and good compatibility with other elastomers chloroprene rubber is widely used in automobile, building, electro-technical, cable, rubber-technical and footwear industries.

The main consumer of PCP is industry of rubber-technical wares. Chloroprene rubbers extruded all other rubber types in production of belts with the most long service period. Very often PCP wares are directly received from latexes after emulsion polymerization. Application fields for synthetic latexes including chloroprene are various and they continuously broaden. Significant part of them are used in production of rubbers and latexes wares (gloves, films), adhesives [201], for improvement of quality of asphalt roads coverings [202], at treatment of natural leather, as grounds for artificial leather production [203].

Radical method of chloroprene polymerization allows to control its technological properties for concrete wares [14, 204]. In particular, we speak about liquid PCP. Wares on its base keep all properties of rubbers on the base of highmolecular PCP.

Properties and Application of Copolymers

More wide application in comparison with *trans*-homopolydienes copolymers containing units of 1,4-*trans*-polydienes are found, firstly PB.

Butadiene copolymerizes with other monomers practically by all known methods (radical, ion, ion-coordinating). The aim is the increase of PB strength properties, to impart high oil- and benzine-resistance, adhesion and other special properties. Copolymers of butadiene with styrene [205, 206] or α–methylstyrene, (meth)acrylonitryl, methylmethacrylate and with vinylpyridine derivatives are of the biggest practical importance. PB units in them are predominantly of 1,4-*trans*-configuration, that associated firstly with radical mechanism of these copolymers formation.

Among copolymers synthesized under the action of stereospecific ion-coordinating systems (vanadium complex catalysts) alternating copolymers are principally novel, for example of butadiene with ethylene [207] and propylene [208, 209], in which butadiene units are in 1,4-*trans*-configuration. Dictinctive feature of such copolymers is availability of six carbon atoms in elemental unit and of side methyl group in the case of copolymerization with propylene. In general, butadiene–propylene rubber can be considered as perspective elastomer for tire and rubber-technical industry, where high elasticity at low temperatures and high resistance to heat ageing are necessary [15].

Under copolymerization of bs with isoprene on chromium-oxide catalyst statistic 1,4-*trans*-copolymers are received; when isoprene units content is 20-90% they are amorphous. Unextendered vulcanizates of crystalline copolymer with 10% of isoprene are characterized by high Yung model and strength at tension [184].

Because of "live" chains mechanism of polymerization of dienes on organochromium derivatives there is possibility of novel polymers of thermoplastic type synthesis. Thus, by consecutive introduction to the system of butadiene and isoprene block-copolymer can be obtained, in which crystalline PB part melts at 125-140°C, and elastic part is a statistic amorphous butadiene *trans*-copolymer with isoprene with glass transition temperature -90°C [1].

Elastomeric copolymers of butadiene and pentadiene in which units of both dienes have *trans*-configuration are characterized by high cohesion strength and adhesion [209], durability to mechanical and thermooxidation destruction [210] and are used in tire production [101, 210]. Rubbers received by copolymerization of butadiene with other conjugated dienes (isoprene, pentadiene) contain in butadiene part 80-95% of 1,4-*trans*-units; they can be used as coverings for golf balls [205], as gyps substitute in orthopedy, for production of nets for perukes and other aims [211, 212].

Table 1. Microstructure of polymers synthesized by radical diene polymerization [1]

Diene	T, °C	Units content, %			
		1,4-*cis*-	1,4-*trans*-	1,2-	3,4-
Butadiene	-35	0	83	17	-
	5	10	72	18	-
	50	21	60	19	-
	100	27	51	22	-
Isoprene	-47	0	86	8	6
	50	8	80	7	5
	100	23	66	5	6
cis-Pentadiene	20	75*		20	5
trans-Pentadiene	20	70*		25	5
2,3-dimethybutadiene	65	96*		4	-
Chloroprene	-40	5	94	0,7	0,3
	40	10	86,5	2,5	1

* Summery content of 1,4-*cis*- and 1,4-*trans*-units.

Table 2. Titanium catalytic systems of stereospecific 1,4-*trans*-polymerization of dienes

Components of the system			Units content,%			References
I	II	modificator	1,4-*cis*	1,4-*trans*	1,2-(3,4-)	
Butadiene						
$TiCl_4$	AlR_3		0	98	2	[49]
$TiCl_4$	$AlEt_3$		6	91	3	[50]
$TiCl_4$	$AlEt_3/I_2$	THT*	13	78	9	[55]
(α,γ,δ) $TiCl_3$	AlR_3			>95		[49]
α-$TiCl_3$	AlR_3		4	90	6	[51]
$TiCl_2$	AlR_3		-	88	12	[56]
$Ti(OR)_4$	AlR_2Cl		4	94	2	[49]
$Ti(OBu)_4$	$AlEt_2Cl$			>98		[57]
$Ti(OR)_4$	AlR_2Cl			>90		[58]
$Ti(NR'_2)_4$	AlR_2Cl			>90		[49]
Isoprene						
α -$TiCl_3$	$AlEt_3$		-	91	9	[59]
γ -$TiCl_3$	$AlEt_3$	$(i\text{-}Pr)_2O$		>90		[60]
$TiCl_2$	$AlEt_3$		-	88	12	[61]
$Ti(i\text{-}OR)_4$	$Al(i\text{-}Bu)Cl_2$	Bu_3N		>90		[62]
$Ti(t\text{-}OBu)_4$	$Al(i\text{-}Bu)Cl_2$	Bu_3N		>90		[62]
Pentadiene						
γ-$TiCl_3$· ·0,33$AlCl_3$	$Al(Et)_3$		-	88	12	[63]

* THT – tetrahydrothiophene.

Table 3. Titanium–magnesium catalysts of 1,4-*trans*-polymerization of dienes

Catalyst components on the base of $TiCl_4/MgCl_2$	Monomer	Polymerization temperature, °C	Additives	Microstructure,%			References
				1,4-*cis*-	1,4-*trans*-	1,2-	
$Al(i\text{-}Bu)_3$	Isoprene	60	-		>90		[77]
$Al(i\text{-}Bu)_3$	Butadiene	20	-	6	82	12	
$Al(i\text{-}Bu)_3$	Isoprene	20	-	-	94	-	[76]
SiO_2 / $Al(i\text{-}Bu)_3$	Isoprene	20	-	-	94	-	
SiO_2 / $Al(i\text{-}Bu)_3$	Butadiene	20	-	-	94	6	[76, 78]
$ZrCl_4/SiO_2/$ $Al(i\text{-}Bu)_3$	Butadiene	30	-	10	81	9	
$Al(i\text{-}Bu)_3$	Isoprene	30	Bu_2O	-	98	-	[79]
$Al(i\text{-}Bu)_2Cl/$ $Al(i\text{-}Bu)_3$	Isoprene	30	Bu_2O	-	98	-	[80]
$AlEt_3$	Isoprene	50	Ph(CO)Et	-	95	-	[81]
$Al(i\text{-}Bu)_3Cl/$ $Al(i\text{-}Bu)_3$	Butadiene	40	EtOH	-	98	2	[82]

Table 4. Vanadium catalytic systems of *trans*-polymerization of dienes

Catalytic system	Al:V	Content of 1,4-*trans*-units, %	References
	Butadiene		
VCl_3–$AlEt_3$	5,3	99	[52]
VCl_3–$AlEt_3$	3	96	[87]
VCl_3–AlR_3	2-3,5	98	[87]
VCl_3–$ZnEt_2$	5	>90	[53]
VCl_3–$AlCl_3$	1	>90	[89]
VCl_4–$AlEt_3$	3	95	[88]
VCl_4–AlR_3	2-3	96	[73]
VCl_4–$AlEt_2Cl$	5	97	[88]
$VOCl_3$–$AlEt_3$	2-3	93	[88]
$VOCl_3$–$AlEt_3$	2-3	90	[73]
$VOCl_3$–$AlEt_2Cl$	~10	97	[88]
$V(C_5H_7O)_3$–$AlEt_2Cl$	70	>90	[90]
	Isoprene		
VCl_3–$AlEt_3$	5-7	>90	[91]
VCl_3–$AlEt_3$	2	97	[92]
VCl_3–$AlEt_3$	3	100	[87]
VCl_3–AlR_3	2	98	[93]
VCl_3–$AlEt_{33}$+$(i\text{-}Pr)_2O$	2	>90	[91]
VCl_3–$Al(i\text{-}Bu)_3$	6,9	>90	[94]
VCl_3–$Al(i\text{-}Bu)_3$ + caoline	2	99	[95]
VCl_3–$Al(i\text{-}Bu)_3$-TiO_2	5,5	>95	[96]
VCl_3–$Al(i\text{-}Bu)_3$+ amines	6,9	>95	[94]
VCl_4–$Al(i\text{-}Bu)_3$	2-3	95	[88]
VCl_4–$Al(i\text{-}Bu)_3$	2	96	[95]
VCl_4–AlR_3	2-3	95	[88]
$VOCl_3$–$AlEt_3$	1	91	[97]
$VOCl_3$–$Al(i\text{-}Bu)_3$	1	80	[95]
$VOCl_3$–$Al(i\text{-}Bu)_3$	1,5-2	84	[86]
	Pentadiene		
VCl_3–$AlEt_3$	2,5	99	[1]
VCl_3–$AlEt_3$	2,8	100	[87]

Table 5. Catalytic systems of diene 1,4-*trans*-polymerization on the base of two transition metals compounds

Components of system			Molar ratio		1,4-*trans*-units, %	References
I	II	III	II:I	III:I		
Butadiene						
VCl_4	$TiCl_4$	$Al(i\text{-}Bu)_3$			>90	[152]
VCl_4	$TiCl_4$	AlR_3+LiR	0,05	2	90	[149]
$V(C_7H_{15}COO)Cl_3$	$Ti(OBu)_4$	$AlEt_3$	0,6	10	>85	[158]
$V(C_7H_{15}COO)Cl_3$	$TiCl_4$	$AlEt_3$	0,4	6,3	>85	[158]
VCl_3+TiO_2	$TiCl_4$	$Al(n\text{-}Pr)_3$	0,5	5	>85	[153]
VCl_4	$TiCl_4$	$AlEt_3$* +$AlEt_3$	1	0,8+6	>95	[159]
VCl_4	α-$TiCl_3$	$AlEt_3$* +$AlEt_3$	1	0,4+20	>95	[160, 161]
Isoprene						
VCl_4	$TiCl_4$	$AlEt_3$	1	5	100	[162]
VCl_4	$TiCl_4$	$Al(i\text{-}Bu)_3$	0,05	2	98	[152]
VCl_3	$TiCl_4$	$Al(i\text{-}Bu)_3$	0,5	10	96	[163]
VCl_4	$TiCl_4$	$AlEt_3$*+ $AlEt_3$	4	0,6+5	95	[54]
Pentadiene						
$VOCl_3$	$TiCl_4$	$Al(i\text{-}Bu)_3$* + $Al(i\text{-}Bu)_3$	0,4	0,6+4	97	[145]
$VOCl_3$	$TiCl_4$	$Al(i\text{-}Bu)_3$* +$Al(i\text{-}Bu)_3$	0,4	1,2+4	74	[145]
$VOCl_3$	$TiCl_4$	$Al(i\text{-}Bu)_3$ +$Al(i\text{-}Bu)_3$	0,4	1,6+4	95	[145]

* After introduction of the first portion of $Al(Et)_3$ or $Al(i\text{-}Bu)_3$* thermal treatment was carried out and then the rest amount of cocatalyst was added.

REFERENCES

1. Dolgoplosk B.A., Tinyakova E.I. *Metalloorganicheskii Kataliz v Protsessach Polymerizatsii* (Organometallic Catalysis in Polymerization Processes). Moscow: Nauka, 1985.
2. G. Henrici-Olive, S. *Olive Coordination and Catalysis.*: Verlag Chemie. GmbH, D-6940 Weinheim, 1977.
3. Hanlon T.L., Kavchok R.W., Bauer R.G. // *J. Am. Chem. Soc., Polym. Prepr.*, 1975, vol.16, no. 1, P.193.
4. Petit A., Cung M.T. // *Conv. Ital. Sci. Macromol.* 1983. V.2. no. 6. P.117.
5. Yoshii F., Hayakawa N., Tocshihiko A. // *Kobunshi ronbunshu*, 1975, vol. 32, no. 12, P.717.
6. Miyata M., Takemoto K. // *J. Macromol. Sci. A.*, 1978, vol. 12, no. 5, P.537.
7. Gueorguiev S.K., Evloguieva K.A. // *Doklady AN Bulgaria*, 1975, vol. 28, no. 8, P.1073.
8. Miyata M., Noma F., Osaki Y., Takemoto K., Kamachi M. // *J. Polym. Sci., Polym. Lett.*, 1986, vol. 24, no. 9, P.457.
9. Sozzani P., Silvestro G.D., Grassi M., Farina M. // *Macromolecules*, 1984, vol. 17, no. 12, P.2532.
10. Audisio G., Silvani A., Zetta L. // *Macromolecules*, 1984, vol. 17, no. 1, P.29.
11. Brockhues F.B., Miller K.L. *Pat. 3190865 USA*. 1965.
12. Lawrence T. *Pat. 3393187 USA*. 1968.
13. Hohmann G., Konter W., Mullere E., Musch R., Wendling P. *Pat. 4786698 USA*. 1988.
14. Kiyonobu M., Hideji O., Yasuaki S. *Pat. 3919281 USA*. 1975.
15. *Syntheticheskii Kauchuk* / Ed. by Garmonov I.V. Leningrad: Khimiya, 1983.
16. Enikolopyan N.S., Oleinik E.F. // *Entsiklopediya Polimerov*. M: Sovetskaya Entsiklopediya, 1972, vol. 1, P. 973.
17. Gaylord N.G., Matyska B., Mach K., Vodehnal J. // *J. Polym. Sci., Polym. Chem.*, 1966, vol. 4, no. 10, P.2493.
18. Denisova T.T., Livshitz I.A.,Gershtein E.R. // *Vysokomol. Soed.*, 1974, Ser. A, vol. 16, no. 4, P.880.
19. Richardson W.S. // *J. Polym. Sci.*, 1954, vol. 13, no. 70, P.325.
20. Kennedy J.P., Marechal E. *Carbocationic Polymerization*. New York: Wiley, 1982.
21. Ferington T.E., Tobolsky A.V. // *J. Polym. Sci.*, 1958, vol. 31, no. 122, P.25.
22. *The Chemistry of Cationic Polymerization* / Ed. by P.H.Plesh. Oxford; London; New York; Paris: Pergamon Press, 1963.
23. Kolbasov V.F., Kutepov D.F., Kul'chitzkii V.I., Sanina N.N. // *Jhurnal Prikladnoi Khimii*, 1984, no. 3, P.631.
24. Babkina M.M., Dobrovinskii L.A., Martynenkova R.A., Yablonovskaya S.D., Shamaev V.S., Yunitzkii I.N., LivshitzR.M.., Doletzkaya G.A. // *Lakokrasochnye Materialy i ich Primenenie*, 1981, no. 6, P.9.
25. Minsker K.S., Zakharov V.P., Mullagaliev I.R., Monakov Yu.B., Berlin A.A.. // *Jhurnal Prikladnoi Khimii*, 2000, vol. 73, no. 11, P.1895.
26. Szwarc M., F.R.S. *Carbanions Living Polymers and Electrone Transfer Process* N.Y.; London; Sydney; Toronto: Interscience publication, J. Wiley and Sons. 1978.

27. Beilin S.J., Dolgoplosk B.A., Tinyakova E.I. // *Eur. Polym.J.*, 1975, vol. 11, no. 5, P.409.
28. Rozinova V.A.. *Cand. Sci. (Chem.) Dissertation*, Leningrad: S.V. Lebedev's VNIISK, 1985.
29. Friedmann G., Brini M., Deluzarche A., Meillard A. // *Bull. Soc. Chim.* France, 1965, no. 12, P.3636.
30. Livshitz I.A..,Denisova T.T.. // *Dokl. Akad. Nauk SSSR*, 1968, vol. 179, no. 1, P.98.
31. Arest-Yakubovich A.A. // *Uspehi Khimii*, 1981, vol. 50, no. 6, P.1141.
32. Baidakova Z.M., Nakhmanovich B.I., Arest-Yakubovich A.A. // *Dokl. Akad. Nauk SSSR*, 1976, vol. 230, no. 1, P.114.
33. Zolling R.J. // *J. Chem. Phys.*, 1969, vol. 50, no. 10, P.4251.
34. Baidakova Z.M., Kristal'nyi V.E., Arest-Yakubovich A.A. // *Vysokomol. Soed.*, A, 1976, vol. 18, no. 9, P.2036.
35. Kaufmann F., Alev S., Collet A., Shue F. // *Eur. Polym. J.*, 1976, vol. 12, no. 4, P.209.
36. Dall'Asta G., Mazzanti G., Natta G., Porri L. // *Makromol. Chem.*, 1962, B.56, no. 2, S.224.
37. Natta G., Dall'Asta G., Mazzanti G., Motroni G. // *Makromol. Chem.*, 1963, B.69, no. 1, S.163.
38. Dall'Asta G. // *J. Polym. Sci. Part A-1: Polym. Chem.*, 1968, vol. 6, no. 8, P.2397.
39. Dall'Asta G., Motroni G. // *J. Polym. Sci. Part A-1: Polym. Chem.*, 1968, vol. 6, no. 8, P.2405.
40. Natta G. // *Makromol. Chem.*, 1965, B.81, no. 2, S. 253.
41. Calderon N., Ofstead E.A., Allen J.W. // *J. Polym. Sci. Part A-1: Polym. Chem.*, 1967, vol. 5, no. 9, P.2209.
42. Calderon N., Judy W.A. *Pat. 1124456 Gr.Brit.* 1965.
43. Calderon N., Ofstead E.A., Ward J.P., Allen J.W., Scott K.W. // *J. Am. Chem. Soc.*, 1968, vol. 90, no. 15, P.4133.
44. Kormer V.A. // *Proc. IUPAC Symp. on Macromolecules*. Budapest, 1969. P.31.
45. Gunther G., Haas F., Marwede G., Nutzel K., Oberkirch W., Pampus G., Schon N., Witte J. // *Angew Makromol. Chem.*, 1970, B.14, S.87.
46. Scott K.W., Calderon N., Ofstead E.A., Judy W.A., Ward J.D. // *Adv. Chem. Ser.*, 1969, V.91, P.399.
47. Boor I.J. *Ziegler Natta Catalysis and Polymerizations*. New York; San Francisco: Acad. Press, 1979.
48. Monakov Yu.B., Tolstikov G.A. *Kataliticheskaya Polymerizatsiya 1,3-Dienov* (Catalytic Polymerization of 1,3-Dienes) Moscow: Nauka, 1990.
49. Marina N.G., Monakov Yu.B., Rafikov S.R., Ponomaremko V.I. // *Uspekhi Khimii*, 1983, vol. 52, no. 5, P.733.
50. Natta G., Porri L., Mazzei A., Morero D. // *Chim. e Ind.*, 1959, vol. 41, no. 5, P.398.
51. Natta G., Porri L., Fiore L. // *Gazz. Chim. Ital.*, 1959, vol. 89, no. 3, P.761.
52. Natta G., Porri L., Mazzanti G. *Pat. 3550158 USA*. 1969.
53. Natta G., Porri L., Mazzanti G.. *Pat. 536631 Italy*. 1957.
54. Van Ameregen G.J. // *Adv. Chem. Ser.*, 1966, vol. 52, P.136.
55. Tornqvist E.G.M., Cozewith C. *Pat. 3865749 USA*. 1975.
56. Khodjhemirom V.A., Zabolotskaya E.V., Gantmakher A.R., Medvedev S.S. // *Vysokomol. Soed. Ser. B.*, 1971, vol. 13, no. 6, P.402.

57. Kakuyo M., Miyatake T., Mizunuma K., Yagi Y., Kazuhiro W. *Pat. 5349034 Japan.* 1993.
58. Cucinella S., Mazzei A., Marconi W., Busetto C. // *Kinetics and Mechanism Polyreactions*. Preprs. Budapest, 1969, vol. 2, P.311.
59. Vladimirov A.M., Gavrilova L.A., Krol' V.A. // *Kauchuk i Resina*, 1959, no. 7, P.6.
60. Cooper W., Vayghan G. *Pat. 1007646 Gr. Brit.* 1965.
61. Khodjhemirom V.A., Zabolotskaya E.V., Gantmakher A.R., Medvedev S.S. // *Vysokomol. Soed. Ser. B.*, 1969, vol. 11, no. 12, P.871.
62. Horne S.E., Carman C.J. // *J. Polym. Sci. Part A-1: Polym. Chem.*, 1971, vol. 9, no. 10, P.3039.
63. Minsker K.S., Karpasas M.M., Monakov Yu.B., Mullagaliev I.R. // *Vysokomol. Soed. Ser. B*, 1987, vol. 29, no. 8, P.608.
64. Cucinella S., Mazzei A., Marconi W., Busetto C. // *J. Macromol. Sci. A.*, 1970, vol. 4, no. 7, P.1549.
65. Matsuzaki K., Yasukawa T. // *J. Polym. Sci. Part A-1: Polym. Chem.*, 1967, vol. 5, no. 3, P.521.
66. Monakov Yu.B., Marina N.G., Savel'eve I.G., Rafikov S.R. // *Vysokomol. Soed. Ser. A*, 1981, vol. 23, no. 1, P.50.
67. Turov B.S., Vinogradov P.A., Dolgoplosk B.A., Khranina E.N., Kostina S.I. // *Dokl. Acad. Nauk SSSR*, 1962, vol. 146, no. 5, P.1141.
68. Turov B.S., Vinogradov P.A., Dolgoplosk B.A., Khranina E.N., Kostina S.I. // *Dokl. Acad. Nauk SSSR*, 1963, vol. 151, no. 5, P.1118.
69. Lasis E., Stewart R.A. *Pat. 3196143 USA*. 1965.
70. Naylor Floyd E. *Pat. 3896102 USA*. 1975.
71. Yamamoto K., Omoto Y., Saegusa T., Furukawa J. // *Kogyo Kaguku Zasshi.*, 1961, vol. 68, no. 2, P.362.
72. Tornqvist E.G.M., Cozewith C. *Pat. 3642758 USA*. 1972.
73. Cooper W., Vaughan G. // *Progr. Polym. Sci.*, 1967, vol. 1, no. 1, P.91.
74. Dolgoplosk B.A., Romanov L.M., Erusalimskii B.L., Bogomol'skii V.Ya. // *Dokl. Akad. Nauk SSSR*, 1957, vol. 115, no. 4, P.731.
75. Erusalimskii B.L., Fo-Sun V., Kavunenko A.P. // *Reports thesises of International Symposium on Macromolecular Chemistry*. Moscow, 1960, vol. 2, P.355.
76. Mushina E.A., Gavrilenko I.F., Borodina I.A., Tinyakova E.I., Antipov E.M., Bondarenko G.N., Podol'skii Yu.Ya., Frolov V.M., Gabutdinov M.S., Krentsel' B.A. // *Vysokomol. Soed. Ser. A*, 1996, vol. 38, no. 3, P.453.
77. He Jidong, Huang Baochem, Jaang Feng, Zheng Jianzhong, Xueming T. // *China Synth. Rubber Ind.*, 1996, vol. 19, no. 1, P.37.
78. Antipov E.M., MushinaE.A., Gavrilenko I.F., Shklyaruk B.F., Razumovskaya I.V., Kuptsov S.A., Podol'skii Yu.Ya., Gabutdinov M.S. // *Vysokomol. Soed. Ser. A*, 1997, vol. 39, no. 4, P.639.
79. Nakamura Tosio, Onuma Hirosi, Makino Kenya, Tadahiko Ito. *Request 59-142211* Japan. 1984.
80. Ono Tosio, Makino Takeya, Ito Tadahiko, Hirosi Onuma. *Request 59-189105* Japan. 1984.
81. Yamada Kunitaka, Masaaki Otsuru. *Request 60-190407 Japan*. 1985.
82. Tosotsugu A. *Request 57-191124 Japan*. 1982.

83. Mushina E.A., Gavrilenko I.F., Mardanov R., Makhina T.K., Frolov V.M., Krentzel B.A., Podolsky Y.Y., Tinyakova E.I. // *VIII Intern. Symp. on Reactions Homogeneous and Heterogeneous Catalysts*. 1995. P.89.
84. Maciejewska H., Wietrzynska-Lalak Z. // *Polymery*, 1989, vol. 34, no. 6. P.303.
85. Chirkov N.M, Matkovskii P.E., D'yachkovskii F.S. *Polymerizatsiya na Kompleksnych Metalloorganicheskich Katalizatorakh* (Polymerization on Complex Metalloorganic Catalysts). Moscow: Khimiya, 1976.
86. Shatalov V.P., Krivoshein V.V., Yudin V.P., Israilit L.Ya., Radugina V.N. *Synteticheskii trans-1,4-Poliisopren* (Synthetic *trans*-1,4-Polyisoprene). Moscow: CSIITENeftekhim, 1976, P.49.
87. Natta G., Porri L., Corradini P., Morero D. // *Chim. e Ind.*, 1958, vol. 40, no. 5, P.362.
88. Natta G., Porri L., Mazzei A. // *Chim. e Ind.*, 1959, vol. 41, no. 2, P.116.
89. Miesserov K.T., Kershenbaum I.L., Lobach R.E., Doplgoplosk B.A. // *Vysokomol. Soed. Ser. B*, 1968, vol.10, no. 9, P.673.
90. Karbonaro A. *Pat. 735171 SSSR*. 1980
91. *The Stereo Rubbers* / Ed. by W.M. Saltman: by J. Wiley & Sons, Inc., 1977.
92. Lovering E.G., Wright W.B. // *J. Polym. Sci. Part A-1: Polym. Chem.*, 1968, vol. 8, no. 8, P.2221.
93. Natta G. // *Makromol. Chem.*, 1960, B.35, S.93.
94. Hill R.W., Leawood K. *Pat. 3219650 USA*. 1965.
95. Krivoshein V.V. *Cand. Sci. (Chem.) Dissertation*, Leningrad: S.V. Lebedev's VNIISK, 1980.
96. Lasky J.S., Garner H.K., Ewart R.H. // *Ind. Eng. Chem. Prod. Res. Develop.*, 1962, vol. 1, no. 1, P.82.
97. Petrov G.N., Korotkov A.A. // *Polymerizatsiya Isoprena Kompleksnymi Katalizatorami* (Isoprene Polymerization on Complex Catalysts) Moscow: Khimiya, 1964. P.112.
98. Cooper W., Eaves D., Owen G.D.T., Vaughan G. // *J. Polym. Sci. Part C: Polym. Symp.*, 1963, no. 4, P.211.
99. Cooper W., Smith R.K., Stokes A. // *J. Polym. Sci. Part B: Polym. Lett.*, 1966, vol. 4, no. 5, P.309.
100. Catteral E. *Pat. 3290279 USA*. 1966.
101. Lauretti E., Santarelli G., Canidio A., Cargani L. // *Ind. Gamma.*, 1980, vol. 24, no. 6, P.37.
102. Wilke G. // *Angew.Chem.*, 1956, B.68, no. 8, S.306.
103. Lasky J.S. *Pat.3054754 USA*. 1962.
104. Petrov G.N., Korotkov A.A. // *Dokl. Akad. Nauk SSSR*, 1961, vol. 141, no. 3, P.632.
105. Monakov Yu.B., Rafikov S.R., Minchenkova N.Kh., Mullagaliev I.R., Minsker K.S. // *Dokl. Alad. Nauk SSSR*, 1981, vol. 258, no. 4, P.892.
106. Natta G., Porri L., Carbonaro A. // *Rend. Accad. Naz. Lincei.*, 1961, vol. 31, no. 8, P.189.
107. Zakhar'yan A.A., Fateev O.V., Bondarenko G.N., Bagdasar'yan A.Kh., Makovetskii K.L., Dolgoplosk B.A. // *Dokl. Akad. Nauk SSSR*, 1989, vol. 305, no. 3, P.652.
108. Yuzi Okuzumi *Pat. 642923 Belg*. 1965.
109. Mazzei A., Cucinella S., Marconi W. // *Chim. e Ind.*, 1969, vol. 51, no. 4, P.374.

110. Nekhaeva L.A., Gavrilenko I.F., Rykov S.V., Khodjhaeva V.L., Antipov E.M., Krentsel' B.A., Frolov V.M., Konovalenko N.A., Tikhomirova I.A. // *Vysokomol. Soed.*, 1996, vol. 38, no. 4, P.594.
111. Ricci G., Italia S., Comitani C. // *Polym. Commun.*, 1991, vol. 32, no. 17, P.514.
112. Ricci G., Italia S., Porri L. // *Macromol. Chem. Phys.*, 1994, vol. 195, no. 4, P.1389.
113. Ricci G., Panagia A., Porri L. // *Polymer*, 1996, vol. 37, no. 2, P.363.
114. Throckmorton M.C. *Pat. 526356 USA*. 1975.
115. Throckmorton M.C. *Pat. 3936432 USA*. 1976.
116. Fisher E.O., Lindner H.H. // *J. Organomet. Chem.*, 1964, vol. 1, no. 4, P.307.
117. Castner Kenneth F. *Pat. 5089574 USA*. 1992.
118. Castner Kenneth F. *Pat. 5448002 USA*. 1995.
119. Lazutkin A.M., Vashkevich V.A., Medvedev S.S., Vasil'eva V.N. // *Dokl. Akad. Nauk SSSR*, 1967, vol. 175, no. 4, P.859.
120. Soboleva T.V., Yakovlev V.A., Tinyakova E.I., Dolgoplosk B.A. // *Dokl. Akad. Nauk SSSR*, 1973, vol. 212, no. 4, P.893.
121. Dawans F., Durand J.P. // *Macromol. Synth.*, 1985, vol. 9, P.19.
122. Taube K., Schmidt U., Gehrke J., Anacker U. // *J. Prakt. Chem.*, 1984, vol. 326, no. 1. P.1.
123. Kang Jung W., Poulton Jasow T. *Pat. 5596053 USA*. 1997.
124. Vasil'ev V.A., Kormer V.A., Kalinicheva N.A. // *Vysokomol. Soed. Ser. A*, 1972, vol. 14, no. 3, P.212.
125. Catteral E. *Pat.963879 Gr.Brit.* 1964.
126. Canale A.J., Hewett W.A. // *J. Polym. Sci., Polym. Phys.*, 1964, vol. 2, no. 15, P.1041.
127. Babitskii B.D., Kormer V.A., Poddubnyi I.V., Sokolov V.N., Chesnokova N.N. // *Dokl. Alad. Nauk SSSR*, 1966, vol. 167, no. 6, P.1295.
128. Otsuka Nariyukisuke, Kikuti Tatsuyuki, Sakaguti Akio, Ikeyama Katsu, Kobayasi Sudsuma *Pat. 26706 Japan*. 1967.
129. Gavrilenko I.F., Stefanovskaya N.N., Bondarenko G.N., Tinyakova E.I., Dolgoplosk B.A. // *Dokl. Alad. Nauk SSSR*, 1976, vol. 228, no. 2, P.351.
130. Gavrilenko I.F., Sokolova V.L., Stefanovskaya N.N. // *Vysokomol. Soed. Ser. A*, 1984, vol. 26, no. 5, P.1096.
131. Sokolova V.L., Gavrilenko I.F., Tinyakova E.I., Kofman V.L., Dolgoplosk B.A. // *Vysokomol. Soed. Ser. A*, 1991, vol. 33, no. 2, P.350.
132. Oreshkin I.A., Chernenko G.M., Tinyakova E.I., Dolgoplosk B.A. // *Dokl. Akad. Nauk SSSR*, 1966, vol. 169, no. 5, P.1102.
133. Gallazzi M.C., Bianchi F., Giarrusso A., Porri L. // *Inorg. Chim. Acta.*, 1984, vol. 94, no. 1-3, P.108.
134. Jenkins D.K. // *Polymer*, 1985, vol. 26, no. 1, P.147.
135. Takeshi I., Hattori Y., Yoshihiro I., Mitsuhiro I. *Pat. 4931376 USA*. 1990.
136. Lynch T.I. *Pat. 6018007 USA*. 2000.
137. Chigir N.N., Guzman I.Sh., Sharaev O.K., Tinyakova E.I., Dolgoplosk B.A. // *Dokl. Akad. Nauk SSSR*, 1982, vol. 263, no. 2, P.75.
138. Zavadovskaya E.N., Sharaev O.K., Borisov G.K., Tinyakova E.I., Dolgoplosk B.A. // *Dokl. Akad. Nauk SSSR* 1984, vol. 274, no. 2, P.333.
139. Mazzei A. // *Makromol. Chem.*, 1981, B. 182, no. 4, S.61.

140. Barbier-Baudry D., Bonnet F., Dormond A., Hafid A., Nyassi A., Visseaux M. // *J. of Alloys and Compounds*, 2001, vol. 323, no. 12, P.592.
141. Hsieh H.L., Yeh G.H.C. // *Rubber Chem. Technol.*, 1985, vol. 58, no. 1, P.117.
142. Yang J., Pang S., Ouyang J. // *Gaofenxi Tongxun.*, 1984, no. 1, P.73.
143. Dolgoplosk B.A., Tinyakova E.I., Guzman I.Sh., Smerkin S.P., Bondarenko G.N., Shapiro A.M. // *Dokl. Akad. Nauk SSSR*, 1983, vol. 272, no. 2, P.394.
144. Yeh H.C., Hsieh H.L. // *Am. Chem. Soc., Polym. Prepr.* 1984. V.25. no. 2. P.52.
145. Marina N.G., Duvakina N.V., Monakov Yu.B., Djemolev U.M., Rafikov S.R. // *Vysokomol. Soed. Ser. A*, 1985, vol. 27, no. 6, P.1203.
146. Marina N.G., Duvakina N.V., Sabirov Z.M., Glukhovskoi V.S., Litvin A., Monakov Yu.B. // *Vysokomol. Soed. Ser. A.*, 1997, vol. 39, no. 1, P.163.
147. Henderson J.N., Shaheen F.G. *Pat. 3872071 USA*. 1975.
148. Natta G., Danusso F., Slanesi D. *Pat. 563350 Belg*. 1958.
149. Lasis E. *Pat. 3347839 USA*. 1967.
150. Saltman W.M. *Pat. 3008945 USA*. 1961.
151. Gebauer U., Oberdorfer A., Donner C., Gehrke K. // *Acta Polymerica*, 1990, vol. 41, no. 2, P.121.
152. Shatalov V.P., Yudin V.P., Krivoshein V.V. *Inventor's Certificate 418047 SSSR* 1972.
153. Beauregard R.E. *Pat. 1387061 Gr.Brit.*1975.
154. Hanlon Thomas L. *Pat. 3951936 USA*. 1976.
155. Beauregard R.E. *Pat. 1387061 Gr. Brit.* 1975.
156. Shatalov V.P., Judin V.P., Krivoshein V.V. *Pat. 3808186 USA*. 1974.
157. Krivoshein V.V., Yudin V.P., Shatalov V.P., Mikhat'ev B.I. *Investigation of Isoprene Polymerization on Catalytic System VCl_4 + $TiCl_4$ + triisobutylaluminum*. Voroneg: 1977.
158. *Pat. 1385778 France*. 1965.
159. Maatschappij N.V. *Pat. 881212 Gr.Brit.* 1961.
160. Cooper W., Vaughan G. *Pat. 1024179 Gr.Brit.* 1966.
161. Cooper W., Vaughan G. *Pat. 3288769 USA*. 1966.
162. Carrick W.L., Chasar A.G., Smith J.J. // *J. Am. Chem. Soc.*, 1960. vol. 82, no. 20, P.5319.
163. Makimoto I., Fujii K. *Pat. 1387135 Gr.Brit.*1975.
164. Pantukh B.I., Rozentsvet V.A., Rafikov S.R. // *Izv. Akad. Nauk SSSR*, Ser. Khim., 1982, no. 5, P.1189.
165. Shatalov V.P., Yudin V.P., Krivoshein V.V. *Pat. 1384163 Gr.Brit.* 1974.
166. Rozentsvet V.A. *Cand. Sci. (Chem.) Dissertation*, Ufa: Inst. of Organ. Chem., 1982.
167. Dolidze V.R., Morozova E.I., Pantuch B.I., Rozentsvet V.A. *Inventor's Certificate 987878 SSSR*. 1982..
168. Mullagaliev I.R. *Cand. Sci. (Chem.) Dissertation*, Ufa: Inst. of Organ. Chem., 1980.
169. Martsina V.G. *Cand. Sci. (Chem.) Dissertation*, Ufa: Inst. of Organ. Chem., 1992.
170. Greco A., Perego G., Cesari M., Cesca S. // *J. Appl. Polym. Sci.*, 1979, vol. 23, no. 5, P.1319.
171. Greco A., Perego G., Cesari M., Cesca S. // *J. Appl. Polym. Sci.*, 1979, vol. 23, no. 5, P.1333.
172. Wilchinsky Z.W., Looney R.W., Tornqvist E.G.M. // *J. Catal.*, 1973, vol. 28, P.351.
173. Haward R.N., Roper A.N., Fletcher K.R. // *Polymer*, 1973, vol. 14, no. 8, P.365.

174. Pantukh B.I., Rozentsvet V.A., Monakov Y.B., Rafikov S.R. // *Acta Polym.*, 1983, vol. 34, no. 11/12, P.732.
175. Rafikov S.R., Minsker K.S., Tolstikov G.A., Monakov Yu.B., Mullagaliev I.R., Ikhsanov A.M., Surkov V.D., Legostaeva T.V., Pantuch B.I. *Inventor's Certificate 751043 SSSR*. 1980
176. Pantuch B.I., Rozentsvet V.A., Dolidze V.P., Tolstikov G.A., Monakov Yu.B., Rafikov S.R., Minsker K.S. *Inventor's Certificate 1129777 SSSR*. 1984.
177. Marconi W., Cesca S., Fortuna C.D. // *J. Polym.Sci. Part A: General Papers*., 1965, no. 1, P.123.
178. Yen T.F. // *J. Polym.Sci.*, 1959, vol. 38, no. 133, P.272.
179. Stille J.K., Vessel E.D. // *J. Polym. Sci.*, 1961, V.49, no. 152, P.419.
180. Cuzin D., Chauvin Y., Lefebvre G. // *Eur. Polym. J.*, 1969, vol. 5, no. 2, P.283.
181. Marvel C.S., Nwa C.L. // *J. Polym. Sci.*, 1960, vol. 45, no. 145, P.25.
182. Antipov E.M., Schklyaruk B.F., Stamm M., Fischer E.W. // *Macromol. Chem. Phys.*, 2001, vol. 202, no. 1, P.82.
183. Nir M.M., Cohen R.E. // *Rubber. Chem. Technol.*, 1993, vol. 66, no. 2, P.295.
184. Angert L.G., Demina N.V., Karyakina M.I., Novikova N.A., Pavlov N.N. // *Entsiklopediya Polimerov*. Moscow: Sovetskaya Entsiklopediya, 1972. vol. 1. P.224.
185. Kang J.W., Lynch T.J., Poulton J.T. *Pat. 5580930 USA*. 1996.
186. Bell G.M., Ridlen J.R. *Pat. 4595616 USA*. 1986.
187. Bell G.M., Ridlen J.R. *Pat. 4485218 USA*. 1984.
188. Skorokhodov S.S. *Entsiklopediya Polimerov*. Moscow: Sovetskaya Entsiklopediya, 1972. vol. 1. P.815.
189. *Tekhnika i Nauka 1986*, no. 10, P.35.
190. Novikov A.S., Jherebkova L.S., Devirts E.Ya., Galil-Ogly F.A. // *Kauchuk i Resina*, 1970, no. 5, P.16.
191. Song J.S., Huang B.C., Yu D.S. // *J. Appl. Polym. Sci.*, 2001, vol. 82, P.81.
192. Di Rossi R.R., Holtzapple G.M., Hubbell J.K., Seloover M.H., Verthe J.J. *Pat. 5300577 USA*. 1994.
193. Warrach W., Swinney F.B., Kent E.G. *Pat. 3553051 USA*. 1971.
194. Islamov S.A., Nikitin V.V., Enikeev R.I., Karamyshev V.G., Muchametkulov M.M. *Inventor's certificate 2161937 Russia*. 2001.
195. Jones R.H., Wei Y.K. // *J. Biomed. Mater. Res.*, 1971, no. 1, P.19.
196. Ashok G. // *Indian Plast. Rev.*, 1973, vol. 19, no. 4, P.9.
197. *Pat. 1227053 Gr.Brit.*. 1971.
198. Egoricheva S.A., Rozentsvet V.A., Pantuch B.I., Livshits R.M. // *Promyshlennost' SK, Shin i RTI*, 1985, no. 11, P.7.
199. Liakumovich A.G., Lonshakova T.I., Kirpichnikov P.A. *Inventor's certificate 827467 SSSR*. 1980.
200. Mardykin V.P., Irkhin V.L., Pavlovich A.V., Antipin L.M., Zorin B.M., Zuev V.V., El'kin B.L. // *Jhurnal Prikl. Khimii*, 1984, vol. 57, no. 5, P.1157.
201. Harada Y., Hayashi T., Hisamasa W. *Pat. 5977222 USA*. 1999.
202. Christell L.A. *Pat. 5087652 USA*. 1992.
203. Trofimovich D.P., Chernaya V.V., Shepelev M.I., Kosmodem'yanskii L.V. // *Entsiklopediya Polimerov*. Moscow: Sovetskaya Entsiklopediya, 1977. vol. 2. P.46.

204. Bieshev Ya.Kh., Svirskii S.E., Monakov Yu.B., Lyapina N.K., Tolstikov G.A. // *Dokl. Akad. Nauk*, 1988, vol. 301, no. 2, P.362.
205. Otake Nobuyuki, Kikuti Mititsugu, Nisihasi Syudzi, Osima Noboru, Furuta Isao *Request 58-225140 Japan*. 1982.
206. Kawakami K. *Pat.4510291 USA*. 1985.
207. Arnold M., Wohlfarth L., Reubner J. *Pat. 3012217 DDR*. 1992.
208. Bauer R.R. *Pat. 5229462 USA*. 1993.
209. Bruzzone M., Carbonaro A., Gargani L. // *Rubber Chem. and Technol.*, 1978, vol. 51, no. 5, P.907.
210. Sandstron P.H., Segatta T.J., Massie J.D. *Pat. 5386865 USA*. 1995.
211. Hirosi O. *Request 59-102907 Japan*. 1985.
212. Noriaki T. *Pat. 2511021 France*. 1983.

Chapter 4

POLYHALOGENATED FLAME RETARDANTS AND DIOXINS

S.M. Lomakin and G.E. Zaikov
Institute of Biochemical Physics of Russian Academy of Sciences,
Moscow, Russia

Flame-retardant systems for synthetic or organic polymers act in five basic ways: (1) gas dilution; (2) thermal quenching; (3) protective coating; (4) physical dilution; (5) chemical interaction; or through a combination of these mechanisms.

1. Inert gas dilution involves using additives that produce large volumes of non-combustible gases on decomposition. These gases dilute the oxygen supply to the flame or dilute the fuel concentration below the flammability limit. Metal hydroxides, metal salts and some nitrogen compounds function in this way.
2. Thermal quenching is the result of endothermic decomposition of the flame retardant. Metal hydroxides, metal salts and nitrogen compounds act to decrease surface temperature and the rate of burning.
3. Some flame retardants form a protective liquid or char barrier. This limits the amount of polymer available to the flame front and/or acts as an insulating layer to reduce the heat transfer from the flame to the polymer. Phosphorus compounds and intumescent systems based on melamine and other nitrogen compounds are examples of this category.
4. Inert fillers (glass fibres and microspheres) and minerals (talc) act as thermal sinks to increase the heat capacity of the polymer or reduce its fuel content.
5. Halogens and some phosphorus flame retardants act by chemical interaction. The flame retardant dissociates into radical species that compete with chain-propagating steps in the combustion process.

Chemicals that are used as flame retardants can be inorganic, organic, mineral, halogen-containing or phosphorus-containing.

Halogenated products are based primarily on chlorine and bromine. This group represents a large volume of the worldwide production. Halogenated flame retardants can be divided into three classes: aromatic, aliphatic and cycloaliphatic. Bromine and chlorine compounds are the only halogen compounds having commercial significance as flame-retardant chemicals. Fluorine compounds are expensive and, except in special cases, are ineffective because the C-F bond is too strong. Iodine compounds, although effective, are expensive and too unstable to be useful [1]. The brominated flame retardants are much more numerous than the chlorinated types because of their higher efficacy [2].

With repect to processability, halogenated flame retardants vary in their thermal stability. In general, aromatic brominated flame retardants are more thermally stable than chlorinated aliphatics, which are more thermally stable than brominated aliphatics. Brominated aromatic compounds can be used in thermoplastics at fairly high temperatures without the use of stabilizers and at very high temperatures with stabilizers. The thermal stability of the chlorinated and brominated aliphatics is such that, with few exceptions, they must be used with thermal stabilizers, such as a tin compound.

Halogenated flame retardants are either added to or reacted with the base polymer. Additive flame retardants are those that do not react in the application designated. There are a few compounds that can be used as an additive in one application and as a reactive in another; tetrabromobisphenol A is the most notable example. Reactive flame retardants become a part of the polymer either by becoming a part of the backbone or by grafting onto the backbone. The choice of a reactive flame retardant is more complex than the choice of an additive type. Synergists such as antimony oxides are frequently used with halogenated flame retardants.

Natural or synthetic material that burns produces potentially toxic products. There has been considerable debate on whether addition of organic flame retardants results in the generation of a smoke that is more toxic and may result in adverse health effects on those exposed. There has been concern in particular about the emission of polybrominated dibenzofurans (PBDF) and polybrominated dibenzodioxins (PBDD) during manufacture, use and combustion of brominated flame retardants.

Combustion of any organic chemical may generate carbon monoxide (CO), which is a highly toxic non-irritating gas, and a variety of other potentially toxic chemicals. Some of the major toxic products that can be produced by pyrolysis of flame retardants are: CO, CO_2, HCl, P_xO_y, ammonia, bromofurans, HBr, HCN, NO_X and phosphoric acid.

In general the acute toxicity of fire atmospheres is determined mainly by the amount of CO, the source of which is the amount of generally available flammable material. Most fire victims die in post flash-over fires where the emission of CO is maximized and the emission of HCN and other gases is less. The acute toxic potency of smoke from most materials is lower than that of CO [3].

Flame retardants significantly decrease the burning rate of the product, reducing heat yields and quantities of toxic gas. In most cases, smoke was not significantly different in room fire tests between flame-retarded and non-flame-retarded products [4].

Morikawa et al. [5] reported toxicity studies on gases from full-scale room fires involving fire retardant materials (a variety, but not specified). HCN and CO were the two major toxicants. There was no evidence that the smoke from flame-retarded materials was more toxic to rabbits than the smoke from non-flame-retarded materials.

Regarding brominated flame retardants, Cullis [2] stated that unless suitable metal oxides or metal carbonates are also present, virtually all the bromine is eventually converted to gaseous hydrogen bromide (HBr). This is a corrosive and powerful sensory irritant. In a fire situation however, it is always carbon monoxide (CO) or hydrogen cyanide (HCN), rather than an irritant which causes rapid incapacitation. Owing to its high reactivity, hydrogen bromide is unlikely to reach dangerously high concentrations [2].

Halogenated dibenzofurans and dibenzodioxins (PBDFs and PBDDs) can be formed from polybrominated diphenyl ethers (PBDEs), polybrominated phenols, polybrominated biphenyls (PBBs) and other brominated flame retardants under various laboratory conditions, including heating. Because chlorinated derivatives are preferably formed during pyrolysis, mixed halogen compounds will be predominantly produced if a chlorine source is also available [6]. As in the case of PCDD/PCDF, it is the 2,3,7,8-substituted isomers that are toxic.

In the late 1980s many pyrolysis experiments (at temperatures of 400-900°C) on brominated flame retardants and flame-retardant systems were performed and the breakdown products measured. Flame retardants or intermediates tested included PBBs, PBDEs, 2,4,6-tribromophenol, pentabromophenol, tetrabromobisphenol A and tetrabromophthalic anhydride [7-11]. Pyrolysis of the flame retardants alone, as well as with polymer mixtures, was investigated [12-14]. Although they indicate which flame retardants are likely to form PBDF (and to a lesser extent PBDD) pyrolysis experiments are not generally comparable to actual fire situations.

Exposure of the general population to flame retardants can occur *via* inhalation, dermal contact and ingestion. Potential sources of exposure are consumer products, manufacturing/disposal facilities and environmental media (including food intake). The same routes are possible for occupational exposure, mainly during production, processing, transportation and disposal/recycling of the flame retardants or the treated products.

Occupational exposure to the breakdown products may also occur during fire fighting. As several of the compounds used are lipophilic and persistent, they may bioaccumulate. Some of the compounds have been shown to cause organ damage, genotoxic effects and cancer.

There is also concern for occupational health and environmental effects from combustion/pyrolysis products, especially the polyhalogenated dibenzofurans and dibenzo-*p*-dioxins, from some organic flame retardants. Other breakdown products also need to be taken into account.

The properties of a number of flame retardants make them persistent and/or bioaccumulative, and they may therefore pose hazards to the environment. Some of the compounds that have been evaluated so far (polybrominated biphenyls, polybrominated diphenyl ethers and chlorinated paraffins) have been found to belong to this group. Some of these have therefore been recommended to not be used.

The availability of relevant data on flame retardants in the open literature is limited, especially for some existing chemicals produced before regulations for commercialization were strengthened in several countries.

A recent study on the risk reduction of halogenated flame retardants (polyhalogenated biphenyls, precursors of dioxins and furans), commissioned by the Organization for Economic Cooperation and Development (OECD), has led to a voluntary industry commitment from the brominated flame retardant manufactures [15]. The key points of this commitment are as follows:

1. There will be no manufacture of polybrominated biphenyls (PBBs), except deca-BB that is manufactured by a single company in Europe. (This will be reviewed in five years.)
2. There will be no manufacture of the non-commercial polybrominated biphenyl ethers (PBBEs).
3. The impurities in deca- and octabromodiphenyl ethers will be minimized.
4. The release of pentabromodiphenyl ether during manufacturing, processing and handling will be minimized.
5. Producers will cooperate with use and end-use industries on the safe disposal of polymers and textiles containing the selected brominated flame retardants.
6. Additional environmental fate studies will be initiated as identified in the World Health Organization's (WHO) International Program on Chemical Safety (IPCS) assessment and the EU Existing Chemicals program.
7. Producers will issue and update product literature to ensure safe handling of these flame retardants at customer and equipment manufacturers.
8. Producers will regularly evaluate the risk of these flame retardants on the basis of the latest information available.

However, there is no scientific justification for phasing out all brominated flame retardants (BFRs). BFRs, which are part of the halogenated flame retardants group, represent a category of 75 flame retardants each with differing structures and properties. The only thing each has in common is the presence of bromine. Only one out of 75 BFRs is widely found in the environment, and this at declining levels. This is penta-BDE for which an EU risk assessment has been completed, leading to a proposal for phase-out in 2003.

The industry fully accepts the proposed phase-out of penta-BDE, as it is based on a comprehensive risk assessment.

In 1991 a Directive was proposed in the EU to limit PBDPO use in articles to 0.1%. The proposed directive was blocked from proceeding by the EU Environment Committee until such time as fire protection safety standards could be formulated and adopted in the EU due to the Committee's concern that adequate alternatives for these products did not exist. In 1994, the European Commission withdrew the Directive from the EU regulatory process on the grounds that it was now out of date. In doing so, the Commission noted that neither Germany nor the Netherlands had proceeded to introduce national rules on the PBDPO and that the "international scientific community is now much less convinced that the PBDPO pose an unacceptable danger to human health and the environment."

On May 2001 the European Committee on the Environment, Public Health and Consumer Policy issued the proposal for a European Parliament and Council directive amending for the 24th time Council Directive 76/769/EEC relating to restrictions on the marketing and use of certain dangerous substances and preparations (pentabromodiphenyl ether).

The last proposal is amended as follows:

By way of derogation these provisions do not apply to technical grade octabromodiphenyl ether provided it contains less than 2% diphenylether, pentabromo derivative (pentaBDE) by mass. This proposal was justified by the contradiction to prohibit the use of pentaBDE as a substance while permitting its residues to be present in significant quantities in other substances. The proposed maximum of 2% pentaBDE as a residue in technical grade octabromodiphenyl ether corresponds to the lowest percentage that allows the production of octabromodiphenyl ether to continue, pending completion of the risk assessment for this substance.

This chapter describes some basic features of dioxins and related compounds and their influence on the environment. The word "dioxin" stands for a group of chemicals that occurs rarely, if ever, in nature. A very large proportion of dioxin comes from human sources. Dioxin began accumulating in the environment around 1900 when the founder of Dow Chemical (in Midland, Michigan) invented a way to split table salt into sodium atoms and chlorine atoms, thus making large quantities of "free chlorine" available for the first time [16]. Initially, Dow considered free chlorine a useless and dangerous waste. But soon a way was found to turn this waste into a useful product, attaching chlorine atoms onto petroleum hydrocarbons and thus creating, during the 1930s and 1940s, a vast array of "chlorinated hydrocarbons." These new chemicals, in turn, gave rise to many of today's pesticides, solvents, plastics, and so forth.

Unfortunately, when these chlorinated hydrocarbons are processed in a chemical plant, or are burned in an incinerator, they release an unwanted byproduct - dioxin - the most toxic family of chemicals ever studied.

Toxicology of DBDPO, OBDPO, PeBDPO and HBCD

The three commercial PBDPO flame retardants are DBDPO, OBDPO and PeBDPO. The potential toxicologic effects of these three products vary with their degree of bromination. That is, in general, the greater the degree of bromination on the diphenyl oxide molecule, the lesser the toxicity of the PBDPO. (This also appears to hold true with the PBB.) Minimal effects are observed with DBDPO in which both aromatic rings are fully brominated. Because of this variation in toxicology associated with the degree of bromination, generalized statements regarding the potential health and environmental effects of the entire class of PBDPO brominated flame retardants are inappropriate.

Decabromodiphenyl Oxide (DBDPO)

The DBDPO commercial product is composed of ≥ 97% DBDPO. DBDPO is a very large molecule with a molecular weight of 959 g/m. DBDPO has undergone a wide range of toxicology tests in mammalian and aquatic species and its toxicology is well characterized (Table 1) [17]. DBDPO is not acutely toxic to mammalian or aquatic species. DBDPO is not irritating to the skin or eye, is not a sensitizer, and does not induce chloracne or hepatic enzymes. The soot and char combustion products from HIPS/DBDPO/Sb_2O_3 are also not acutely toxic and are not chloracnegenic. DBDPO is not a reproductive toxicant and is not teratogenic. DBDPO has a low degree of long-term toxicity that can be attributed to its poor absorption, rapid elimination and capacity to be metabolized. Doses of 10% and 5% of the diet were tolerated with no adverse effects by rats and mice for 14 and 90 days, respectively. Doses of 5% of the diet were tolerated for two years by rats and mice with no effect on body weight or mortality and only minimal evidence of organ effects. Two two year carcinogenicity bioassays have been conducted. The first at a top dose level of 1 mg/kg in rats produced no evidence of carcinogenicity. The second conducted at 2.5 and 5% of the diet in rats and mice produced no, equivocal and some evidence of carcinogenicity depending on genus and sex. DBDPO does not bioconcentrate in fish and can undergo photodegradation (at a very slow rate). DBDPO aqueous photodegradation products are not lower brominated diphenyl oxides. Leaching from polymers is insignificant. DBDPO is not widely distributed in the environment, and where found, is largely confined to sediments near point sources. DBDPO is likely to be highly bound to sediment which, will limit its bioavailability and is unlikely to be toxic or accumulated in sediment-dwelling species. DBDPO is not being detected in fish and water samples. DBDPO is not likely to present a toxicologic risk to wildlife, based on its low degree of toxicity in multiple studies in mammals. DBDPO does not present a bioaccumulation risk based on its physical/chemical properties, and results of laboratory studies and environmental monitoring.

Table 1. DBDPO Toxicology Summary. Comprised of existing data [17].

Test	Results
Oral LD50	> 2,000 mg/kg
Dermal LD50	> 2,000 mg/kg
Inhalation LC50	> 48.2 mg/L
Eye Irritation	Not an irritant
Skin Irritation	Not an irritant
Human Skin Sensitization	Not a skin sensitizer
Ames	Not mutagenic
Mouse Lymphoma	Not mutagenic
Sister Chromatid Exchange	Not mutagenic
Chromosome Aberration	Did not induce aberrations
14 Day Rat & Mice Oral (Diet)	NOEL > 100,000 ppm (10%)
90 Day Rat & Mice Oral (Diet)	NOEL > 50,000 ppm (5%)
Rat 1 Generation Reproduction	NOEL = 100 mg/kg (highest dose tested)
Rat Teratogenicity	NOEL > 1,000 mg/kg
Rat & Mouse Carcinogenicity (Diet)	25,000 (2.5%) or 50,000 (5%) ppm Negative or equivocal evidence of carcinogenicity No effect body weight or mortality Minimal evidence of chronic toxicity
Rat Carcingenicity (Diet)	NOEL > 1 mg/kg (highest dose tested)
Rat Hepatic Enzyme Induction	Did not induce hepatic enzymes
Rabbit Skin Acnegenicity	Not acnegenic; Soot and char not acnegenic
Rat Pharmacokinetics (Oral & IV)	Low bioavailability Poorly absorbed (<1%) from GI tract Rapidly Eliminated with short half life (< 24 hours)
Ready Biodegradation	Not readily biodegradable
Fish LC50	> 500 mg/L
Algae EC50	> 1 mg/L
Fish Bioaccumulation	Not bioaccumulative; BCF<5 (60 ug/L) &<50 (6 ug/L) 6wk
Aqueous Photodegradation	Half life >> 90 days; Products not lower BrDPOs
Polymer Extraction	Negligible

DBDPO Compared to PBB and PCB

DBPDO has been assumed by some to have similar properties and to pose the same potential environmental threats as the polychlorinated biphenyls (PCB) and the polybrominated biphenyls (PBB). This assumption is apparently based on their seemingly similar chemical structures. However, these chemicals in reality are very different from one another.

The first difference between the PCB, PBB and DBDPO are found in their physical/chemical properties. The PCB are liquids. PBB and DBDPO are solids. The lower chlorinated PCB are volatile. The PBB and DBDPO have extremely low vapor pressures and are not volatile. Their molecular weights vary greatly between the different classes. Hexachlorobiphenyl (HxCB) weighs 358 g/m, hexabromobiphenyl (HxBB) weighs 622 g/m, and DBDPO 959 g/m. The great difference in the molecular weights of HxCB and HxBB is due to the difference in weight of chlorine and bromine. Chlorine's atomic weight is 35 whereas bromine's atomic weight is 79. The molecular volumes of the PCB, PBB, and DBDPO are also very different, again due to the influences of chlorine and bromine. Bromine atoms occupy a considerably larger volume than due chlorine atoms.

The above properties greatly influence the bioavailability, absorption and bioaccumulation of the PCB, PBB, and DBDPO in biotic systems. Pharmacokinetic studies show DBDPO has a half life in rats of less than 24 hours [17], whereas less than 10% of the total HxBB dose would ever be excreted by rats [17]. In a study directly comparing the fish bioconcentration of DBDPO, octabromobiphenyl and tetrachlorobiphenyl, DBDPO and octabromobiphenyl were not taken up by the fish whereas the tetrachlorobiphenyl bioconcentrated at least 50 times over the exposure level within 4 hours [18]. In addition, the PCB and PBB effect levels in mammals are considerably lower than those of DBDPO and present a different toxicological picture.

Given that the toxicology of the PCB/PBB/dioxins are generally accepted to be receptor-mediated events, the lack of coplanarity and the orthogonal relationship of the diphenyl rings will not allow DBDPO to induce PCB/PBB/dioxin-like toxicity. There is an additional difference between these molecules resulting from the presence of the ether linkage. The ether linkage causes a 120 degree bend in the alignment of the phenyl rings in the diphenyl oxide molecule. PCB and PBB, having no oxygen link between the two aromatic rings, lacks this bend. Thus, the phenyl rings in the PBDPO cannot adopt a coplanar conformation similar to the toxic PCB and PBB congeners, 2,3,7,8-TCDD, and 2,3,7,8-TBDF. The PBDPO and 2,3,7,8-TCDD/F have distinctly different molecular geometries. The PBDPO are electronically and geometrically dissimilar to 2,2'4,4',5,5'-HxBB due to the presence of the ether linkage.

Another major difference between these chemicals is their use. PCB were used in applications with a high potential for environmental release: as liquids in large volume transformers and capacitors and in paperless copies. As a result of their physical properties and uses, PCB residues are found in many diverse locations around the world [19]. The production, distribution and use of the PBB were not as wide spread as the PCB, and PBB, unlike PCB, were not used in applications with significant potential for release to the environment. A main use of HxBB, was in thermoplastics used as housing for typewriters and business machine and in this use has little tendency to migrate from the thermoplastic [19].

As a result of these differences in properties and uses, environmental contamination with PCB, PBB and DBDPO commercial chemicals is vastly different in magnitude. PCB were steadily released into the environment, in many countries, presumably over decades, and were found to be pervasive, world-wide contaminants as early as 1978 [19]. In addition, the number of PCB reaching the environment probably number nearly 100 different compounds. PBBs, encompassing a small number chemical structures to begin with, are of concern due to a single contamination incident in 1973 in which a hexabromobiphenyl (HxBB) product was accidentally mixed in animal feed and was apparently limited to the State of Michigan [19]. Today, only one PBB, decabromobiphenyl, remains in commercial production. This PBB does not share the properties of HxBB. Finally, DBDPO is not a widespread or diffuse environmental contaminant and its primary use in thermoplastics limits its environmental release and thus environmental exposure [17].

Octabromodiphenyl Oxide (OBDPO)

The molecular weight of the OBDPO molecule is 801 g/m. The commercial OBDPO product is a mixture of PBDPO congeners ranging from penta- to nonabromodiphenyl oxide. Existing data on OBDPO toxicology is summarized in Table 2. [17]. Like DBDPO, OBDPO is not acutely toxic, is not irritating, is not mutagenic and is not bioconcentrating. OBDPO's toxicology data demonstrates its properties on repeated exposure are different from that of DBDPO. OBDPO induced liver effects in 14, 28 and 90 day studies (12 mg/kg for 14 days or 100 mg/kg for 28 days) whereas DBDPO did not at significantly higher levels (10% diet for 14 days). OBDPO was also effective in inducing hepatic enzymes whereas DBDPO was not. OBDPO produced teratogenic effects in the rat, but not the rabbit.

Pentabromodiphenyl Oxide (PeBDPO)

The molecular weight of the PeDPO molecule is 564 g/m. The commercial PeBDPO product is a mixture of PBDPO congeners consisting primarily of tetra- and pentabromodiphenyl oxide. Existing data on PeBDPO toxicology is summarized in Table 3 [17]. Like DBDPO and OBDPO, the PeBDPO commercial product is not acutely toxic, is not irritating and is not mutagenic. Like OBDPO, PeBDPO's toxicology data demonstrates its properties on repeated exposure are different from that of DBDPO. Liver effects were induced at 100 mg/kg in a 28 day study and the NOEL in a 90 day study in rats was 2 mg/kg. PeBDPO was effective in inducing hepatic enzymes and while the commercial mixture was found to bioconcentrate in fish, the major constituent of the product, the pentabromdiphenyl oxide molecule showed no significant accumulation. Further, the solvent dimethylsulfoxide (DMSO) was used in the fish bioconcentration study, which may have enhanced the uptake of the tetrabromodiphenyl oxide congener. DMSO is known for its ability to enhance the absorption of chemicals (including drugs) through the skin.

Table 2. OBDPO Toxicology Summary [17].

Test	Results
Oral LD50	> 28,000 mg/kg
Dermal LD50	> 2,000 mg/kg
Inhalation LC50	> 50 mg/L
Eye Irritation	Not an irritant
Skin Irritation	Not an irritant
Ames	Not mutagenic
Sister Chromatid Exchange	Not mutagenic
Unscheduled DNA Synthesis	Did not induce
28 Day Rat Oral (Diet)	Liver effects @ 100, 1,000, 10,000 mg/kg diet
90 Day Rat Oral (Diet)	Liver effects @ 100, 1,000, 10,000 mg/kg diet
14 Day Rat Inhalation	NOEL = 1.2 mg/m^3
Rat Teratogenicity	Teratogenic; NOEL = 2.5 mg/kg
Rabbit Teratogenicity	Not teratogenic NOEL = 5 mg/kg (fetotoxicity @ maternally toxic dose)
Rat Hepatic Enzyme Induction	Induced hepatic enzymes
Fish Bioaccumulation	BCF < 4 after 8 week exposure period

Table 3. PeBDPO Toxicology Summary [17].

Test	Results
Oral LD50	> 500 mg/kg in CD rats 7,400 or 5,800 mg/kg in male or female Wistar rats, respectively
Dermal LD50	> 2,000 mg/kg
Inhalation LD50	> 200 mg/L
Eye Irritation	Slight irritation
Skin Irritation	Not an irritant
Ames	Not mutagenic
28 Day Rat Oral (Gavage)	Liver effects at 100 and 1,000 mg/kg
90 Day at Oral (Diet)	NOEL = 2 mg/kg
Rat Teratogenicity	Not teratogenic; NOEL maternal toxicity = 100 mg/kg
Rat Hepatic Enzyme Induction	Induced hepatic enzymes
Fish Bioaccumulation	BCF not significant (PeBDPO) BCF > 10,000 (TeBDPO); DMSO interaction

Hexabromocyclododecane (HBCD)

HBCD is a cyclic aliphatic and is structurally distinct from the PBDPO flame retardants. HBCD's molecular weight is 641 g/m. The existing toxicology data on HBCD is summarized in Table 4. [17]. HBCD is not acutely toxic, not irritating and not mutagenic. HBCD is not teratogenic in the rat at a top dose of 1% of the diet. Pharmacokinetics show that HBCD is rapidly absorbed from the gastrointestinal tract of rats and rapidly metabolized and excreted. Over 86% of the dose was eliminated within 72 hours. HBCD's LC/EC50 in fish, daphnia, and algae are greater than HBCD's recently determined water solubility. Negligible migration from foam insulation boards, HBCD's major use, was found.

Table 4. HBCD Toxicology Summary [17].

Test	Results
Oral LD50	> 10,000 mg/kg
Dermal LD50	> 8,000 mg/kg
Inhalation LC50	> 200 mg/L
Eye Irritation	Not an irritant
Skin Irritation	Not an irritant
Ames	Not mutagenic
Rat Teratogenicity (Diet)	NOEL > 10,000 ppm (1%)
Rat Pharmacokinetics (Oral)	Rapidly absorbed from GI tract Rapidly metabolized Eliminated 86% of dose within 72 hr
Chicken Cataractogenicity (Diet)	NOEL > 10,500 ppm (1.5%)
Fish LC50	L. macrochirus >100 mg/L L. idus > 10,000 mg/L
Daphnia EC50	>1000 mg/L (24 hr) and = 146 mg/L (48 hr)
Bacterial EC50	> 10,000 mg/L
Algae EC50	EC50 > water solubility: S. subspicatus > 500 mg/L Chlorella sp. > 1.5 mg/l S. costatum, T. Pseudonana = 9.3 ug/L to 0.37 mg/L
Foam Migration	Negligible

Toxicology testing is on-going on DBDPO, OBDPO, PeBDPO and HBCD per industry's commitments under the EU risk assessment programs.

DIOXINS

Halogenated dibenzo-*p*-dioxins and related compounds (commonly known simply as dioxins) are contaminants present in a variety of environmental media. This class of compounds has caused great concern in the general public as well as intense interest in the scientific community. Much of the public concern revolves around the characterization of these compounds as among the most potent man-made toxicants ever studied. Indeed, these compounds are extremely potent in producing a variety of effects in experimental animals based on traditional toxicology studies at levels hundreds or thousands of times lower than most chemicals of environmental interest. In addition, human studies demonstrate that exposure to dioxin and related compounds is associated with subtle biochemical and biological changes whose clinical significance is as yet unknown and with chloracne, a serious skin condition associated with these and similar organic chemicals.

This chapter describes some basic features of dioxins and related compounds and their influence on the environment. The word "dioxin" stands for a group of chemicals that occurs rarely, if ever, in nature. A very large proportion of dioxin comes from human sources. Dioxin began accumulating in the environment around 1900 when the founder of Dow Chemical (in Midland, Michigan) invented a way to split table salt into sodium atoms and chlorinc atoms, thus making large quantities of "free chlorine" available for the first time [16]. Initially, Dow considered free chlorine a useless and dangerous waste. But soon a way was found to turn this waste into a useful product, attaching chlorine atoms onto petroleum hydrocarbons and thus creating, during the 1930s and 1940s, a vast array of "chlorinated hydrocarbons." These new chemicals, in turn, gave rise to many of today's pesticides, solvents, plastics, and so forth.

Laboratory studies suggest the probability that exposure to dioxin-like compounds may be associated with other serious health effects including cancer. Recent laboratory studies have provided new insights into the mechanisms involved in the impact of dioxins on various cells and tissues and, ultimately, on toxicity. Dioxins have been demonstrated to be potent modulators of cellular growth and differentiation, particularly in epithelial tissues.

Chemical Structure and Properties

Polychlorinated dibenzodioxins (PCDDs), polychlorinated dibenzofurans (PCDFs), and polychlorinated biphenyls (PCBs) are chemically classified as halogenated aromatic hydrocarbons. The chlorinated and brominated dibenzodioxins and dibenzofurans are tricyclic aromatic compounds with similar physical and chemical properties, and both classes are similar structurally. Certain of the PCBs (the so-called coplanar or mono-ortho coplanar congeners) are also structurally and conformationally similar. The most widely studied of these compounds is 2,3,7,8- tetrachlorodibenzo-*p*-dioxin (TCDD). This compound, often called simply dioxin, represents the reference compound for this class of compounds. The structure of TCDD and several related compounds is shown in Figure 1.

Dioxin-like compounds are defined to include the subset of this class of compounds, which are generally agreed to produce dioxin-like toxicity. These compounds are assigned individual toxicity equivalence factor (TEF) values as defined by international convention [20]. Results of *in vitro* and *in vivo* laboratory studies contribute to the assignment of a relative toxicity value. TEFs are estimates of the toxicity of dioxin-like compounds relative to the toxicity of TCDD, which is assigned a TEF of 1.0. All chlorinated dibenzodioxins (CDDs) and chlorinated dibenzofurans (CDFs) with chlorines substituted in the 2,3,7, and 8 positions are assigned TEF values. Additionally, the analogous brominated dioxins and furans (BDDs and BDFs) and certain polychlorinated biphenyls have recently been identified as having dioxin-like toxicity and thus are also included in the definition of dioxin-like compounds. Generally accepted TEF values for chlorinated dibenzodioxins and dibenzofurans are shown in Table 5.

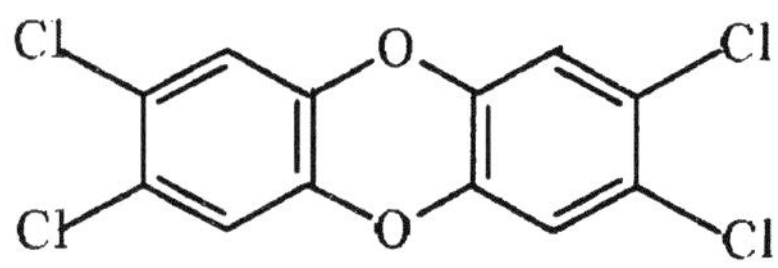

2,3,7,8-Tetrachlorodibenzo-*p*-dioxin

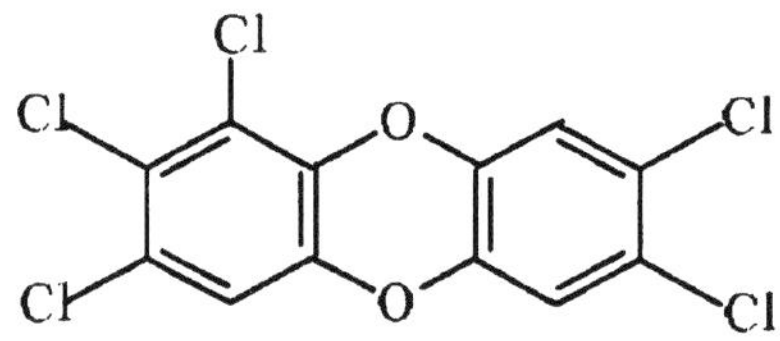

1,2,3,7,8-Pentachlorodibenzo-*p*-dioxin

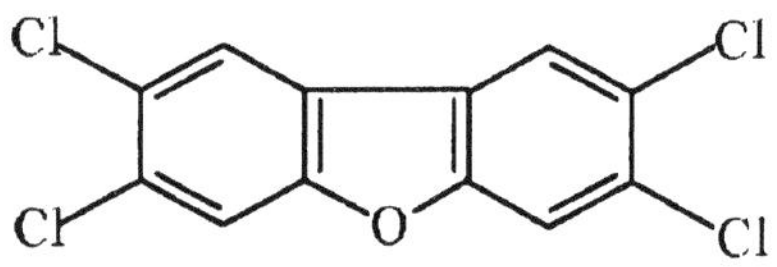

2,3,7,8-Tetrachlorodibenzofuran

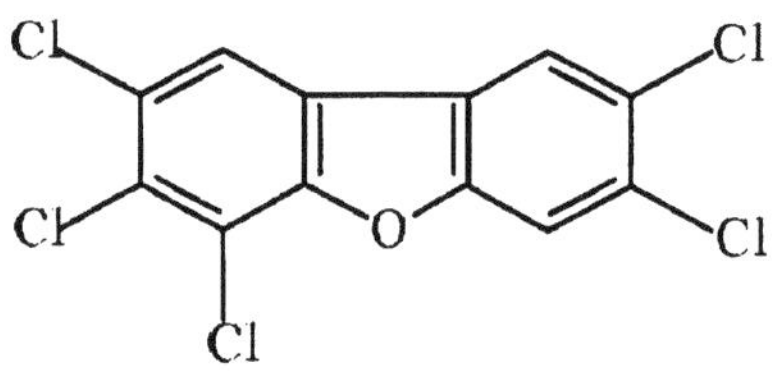

2,3,4,7,8-Pentachlorodibenzofuran

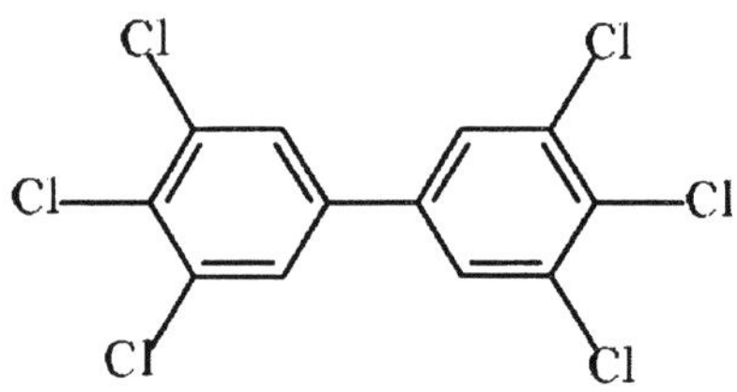

3,3',4,4',5,5'-Hexachlorobiphenyl

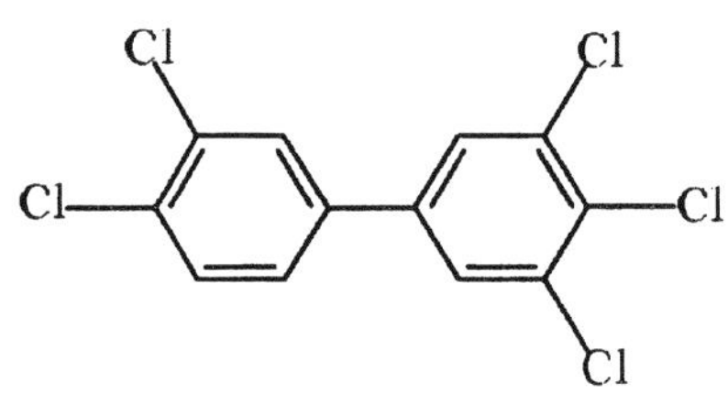

3,3',4,4',5,'-Pentachlorobiphenyl

Figure 1. The structures of dioxin and similar compounds.

Table 5. Toxicity Equivalence Factors (TEFs) for CDDs and CDFs [21].

Compound	Toxicity Equivalence Factor (TEF)
Mono-, Di-, and Tri-CDDs	0
2,3,7,8-TCDD	1
Other TCDDs	0
1,2,3,7,8-PeCDD	0.5
Other PeCDDs	0
1,2,3,4,7,8-HxCDD	0.1
Other HxCDDs	0
1,2,3,4,7,8,9-HpCDD	0.01
Other HpCDDs	0
Mono-, Di-, and Tri-CDFs	0
2,3,7,8-TCDF	0.1
Other TCDFs	0
1,2,3,7,8-PeCDF	0.05
2,3,4,7,8-PeCDF	0.5
Other PeCDFs	0
1,2,3,4,7,8-HxCDF	0.1
Other HxCDFs	0
1,2,3,4,7,8,9-HpCDF	0.01
Other HpCDFs	0
OCDF	0.001

A World Health Organization/International Program on Chemical Safety meeting held in The Netherlands in December 1993 considered the need to derive internationally acceptable interim TEFs for the dioxin-like PCBs. Recommendations arising from that meeting of experts [21] suggest that in general only a few of the dioxin-like PCBs are likely to be significant contributors to general population exposures to dioxin-like compounds. Dioxin-like PCBs may be responsible for approximately one-fourth to one-half of the total toxicity equivalence associated with environmental exposures to this class of related compounds. Both the refinement of the toxicity equivalence factors for dioxin-like PCB congeners [22] as well as a compilation and analysis of all available data on relative toxicities of dioxin-like PCBs with respect to a number of end points [21] support these findings. Although these findings have been published recently, additional review and data collection will be needed. In addition, this panel urged investigation of companion TEFs for ecotoxicological use, based on data from ecotoxicological studies. The concentrations of dioxin and related compounds will be presented as TEQs. TEQs are determined by summing the products of multiplying concentrations of individual dioxin-like compounds times the corresponding TEF for that compound. At times, levels will be presented as presented as concentration of CDDD because many past studies monitored this congener alone. There are 75 individual compounds comprising the CDDs, depending on the positioning of the chlorine(s), and 135 different CDFs. These are called individual congeners. Likewise, there are 75 different positional congeners of BDDs and 135 different congeners of BDFs. Only 7 of the 75 congeners of CDDs or of BDDs are thought to have dioxin-like toxicity; these are ones with chlorine/bromine substitutions in, at least, the 2, 3, 7, and 8 positions. Only 10 of the 135 possible congeners of CDFs or of BDFs are thought to have dioxin-like toxicity; these also are ones with substitutions in the 2, 3, 7, and 8 positions. While this suggests 34 individual CDDs, CDFs, BDDs, or BDFs with dioxin-like toxicity, inclusion of the mixed chloro/bromo congeners substantially increases the number of possible congeners with dioxin-like activity.

There are 209 PCB congeners. Only 13 of the 209 congeners are thought to have dioxin-like toxicity; these are PCBs with 4 or more chlorines with just 1 or no substitution in the *ortho* position. These compounds are sometimes referred to as coplanar, meaning that they can assume a flat configuration with rings in the same plane. Similarly configured polybrominated biphenyls are likely to have similar properties; however, the data based on these compounds with regard to dioxin-like activity has been less extensively evaluated. Mixed chlorinated and brominated congeners also exist, increasing the number of compounds considered dioxin-like. The physical/chemical properties of each congener vary according to the degree and position of chlorine and/or bromine substitution. Very little is known about occurrence and toxicity of the mixed (chlorinated and brominated) dioxin, furan, and biphenyl congeners.

In general, these compounds have very low water solubility, high octanol-water partition coefficients, and low vapor pressure and tend to bioaccumulate.

ENVIRONMENTAL IMPACT

In soil, sediment, the water column, and probably air, CDDs/CDFs are primarily associated with particulate and organic matter because of their high lipophilicity and low water solubility. They exhibit little potential for significant leaching or volatilization once sorbed to particulate matter. The available evidence indicates that CDDs and CDFs, particularly the tetra- and higher chlorinated congeners, are extremely stable compounds under most environmental conditions, with environmental persistence measured in decades. The only environmentally significant transformation process for these congeners is believed to be photodegradation of chemicals not bound to particles in the gaseous phase or at the soil- or water-air interface. Brominated congeners are significantly more readily transformed by photodegradation. CDDs/CDFs entering the atmosphere are removed either by photodegradation or by dry or wet deposition. Although some volatilization of dioxin-like compounds on soil does occur, the predominant fate of CDDs/CDFs sorbed to soil is to remain in place near the surface of undisturbed soil or to move to water bodies with erosion of soil. CDDs/CDFs entering the water column primarily undergo sedimentation and burial. The ultimate environmental sink of these CDDs/CDFs is believed to be aquatic sediments.

Little information exists on the environmental transport and fate of the dioxin-like PCBs. However, the available information on the physical/chemical properties of dioxin-like PCBs, coupled with the body of information available on the widespread occurrence and persistence of PCBs in the environment, indicates that these PCBs are likely to be associated primarily with soils and sediments and to be thermally and chemically stable. Soil erosion and sediment transport in water bodies and emissions to the air (via volatilization, dust resuspension, or point source emissions) followed by atmospheric transport and deposition are believed to be the dominant transport mechanisms responsible for the widespread environmental occurrence of PCBs. Photodegradation to less chlorinated congeners followed by slow anaerobic and/or aerobic biodegradation is believed to be the principal path for destruction of PCBs. Similar situations exist for the polybrominated biphenyls (PBBs).

SOURCES

PCBs were produced in relatively large quantities for use in such commercial products as dielectrics, hydraulic fluids, plastics, and flame retardants. A similar situation exists for the commercially produced PBBs, which were produced for a number of uses like flame retardants.

Dioxin-like compounds are released to the environment in a variety of ways and in varying quantities, depending on the source. This trend suggests that the presence of dioxin-like compounds in the environment has occurred primarily as a result of industrial practices and is likely to reflect changes in release over time.

Although these compounds are released from a variety of sources, the congener profiles of CDDs and CDFs found in sediments have been linked to combustion sources [23]. Three theories have been suggested to explain formation of CDDs and CDFs during combustion [24]: (1) CDDs and CDFs are present in the fuels or feed materials and pass through the combustion intact; (2) precursor chemicals are present in the fuels or feed material and undergo reactions catalyzed by particles and other chemicals to form CDDs and CDFs; and (3) the CDDs and CDFs are formed *de novo* from organic and inorganic substrates bearing little resemblance in molecular structure.

The principal identified sources of environmental release of CDDs and CDFs may be grouped into four major types:

1. Combustion and Incineration Sources: Dioxin-like compounds can be generated and released to the environment from various combustion processes when chlorine donor compounds are present. These sources can include incineration of wastes such as municipal solid waste, sewage sludge, hospital and hazardous wastes; metallurgical processes such as high-temperature steel production, smelting operations, and scrap metal recovery furnaces; and the burning of coal, wood, petroleum products, and used tires for power/energy generation and polymers-FR combustion.

There are three primary mechanisms for CDD/CDF emissions from combustion sources [25]:

Mechanism 1: This refers to CDD/CDFs contained in the feed that pass through the combustor intact and are subsequently released to the environment. For most systems, this is not thought to be a major contributor to CDD/CDF emissions for two reasons. First, for commercial systems with good combustion controls, the temperatures and residence times should result in the destruction of most CDD/CDFs in the feed. Second, mass balance studies of a number of combustion systems show that more CDD/CDFs can be detected downstream of the furnace than in the feed. Consequently synthesis appears to be a more important mechanism than pass through.

Mechanism 2: This is the formation of CDD/CDFs from the thermal breakdown and molecular rearrangement of aromatic precursors either originating in the feed or forming as a product of incomplete combustion. Actual synthesis of CDD/CDF occurs in the postcombustor environment. The CDD/CDFs form when the precursors sorb onto binding sites on the surface of fly ash particles. This reaction has been observed to be catalyzed by the presence of a transition metal sorbed to the particulate. The most potent catalyst is copper chloride. Heat in a range of 200 to 450°C has been identified as a necessary condition for these reactions to occur, with either lower or higher temperatures inhibiting the process. Since these reactions involve heterogenous chemistry, the rate of emissions is less dependent on reactant concentration than conditions that promote formation such as temperature, retention time and availability of catalytic surfaces. For this mechanism to be significant, two broad conditions are needed.

Mechanism 3 : This is the formation of CDD/CDFs in the post-combustion environment in the absence of aromatic precursors. This *de novo* synthesis involves the oxidative breakdown of macromolecular carbon structures (e.g., graphite) leading to the formation of aromatic CDD/CDF precursors. These precursors then undergo the transformations associated with mechanism 2 to form CDD/CDFs. As with mechanism 2, since this mechanism involves heterogenous chemistry, the rate of emissions is dominated by the same physical conditions as discussed in mechanism 2. Mechanisms 2 and 3 can occur simultaneously, share a number of common reaction pathways, occur in the same physical environment and are controlled by many of the same physical conditions. In well designed and operated combustion systems, the precursor species needed for mechanism 2 are not in abundant supply; consequently *de novo* synthesis can become the dominant pathway for formation. In systems with incomplete combustion, it is difficult to sort out the relative contribution of these two mechanisms to total emissions. Both mechanisms, however, can be curtailed if steps are taken to minimize the physical conditions needed to support formation (i.e., time, temperature and reactive surface). The combustion formation chemistry of PCBs is less well-studied than for CDD/CDFs, but it is reasonable to assume that these same three mechanisms would apply. For waste incineration, PCBs can exist in significantly higher concentrations in the feed than CDD/CDFs. Consequently, mechanism 1 may play a more prominent role in PCB emissions from some forms of waste combustion.

2. Chemical Manufacturing/Processing Sources: Dioxin-like compounds can be formed as byproducts from the manufacture of chlorine and such chlorinated compounds as chlorinated phenols (e.g. pentachlorophenol), PCBs, phenoxy herbicides (e.g. 2,4,5-T), chlorinated benzenes, chlorinated aliphatic compounds, chlorinated catalysts, and halogenated diphenyl ethers and other flame retardants.
3. Industrial/Municipal Processes: Dioxin-like compounds can be formed through the chlorination of naturally occurring phenolic compounds such as those present in wood pulp. The formation of CDDs and CDFs resulting from the use of chlorine bleaching processes in the manufacture of bleached pulp and paper has resulted in the presence of CDDs and CDFs in paper products as well as in liquid and solid wastes from this industry. Municipal sewage sludge has been found to occasionally contain CDDs and CDFs.
4. Reservoir Sources: The persistent and hydrophobic nature of these compounds causes them to accumulate in soils, sediments, and organic matter and to persist in

waste disposal sites. The dioxin-like compounds in these "reservoirs" can be redistributed by various processes such as dust or sediment resuspension and transport. Such releases are not original sources in a global sense, but can be on a local scale. For example, releases may occur naturally from sediments through volatilization or from operations that disturb them, such as dredging. Aerial deposition and accumulation on leaves can lead to releases during forest fires or leaf composting operations.

These studies assume that emissions to air make up the major portion of dioxins released to the environment. Estimates of total release in European countries range from approximately 100-

1000 g TEQ/year in West Germany and 100-200 g TEQ/year in Sweden to approximately 1000 and 4000 g TEQ/year maximum emissions in The Netherlands and United Kingdom, respectively. Similar nationwide estimates for the United States have not been compiled prior to this reassessment effort. The Exposure Document estimates the U.S. emissions to be in the range of 3300-26000 g TEQ/year, with a central estimate of 9300 g TEQ/year. These estimates were derived from data from emission tests at relatively few facilities in each combustion class. These data were used to develop emission factors and then extrapolated to a nationwide basis using the total amount of waste feed material in each class. Because of the limited number of measurements and the large number of potential sources for each of these emissions, total estimated emissions from these sources are considered highly uncertain. Diesel-fueled vehicles, hazardous waste burning, forest fires, and metal smelting are more moderate contributors of dioxin-like compounds, but the magnitude of the contribution is also highly uncertain. Sewage waste incineration and residential wood burning as well as a few minor processes round out the current analysis and provide lower range estimates of medium to low certainty.

While all of the above emission and deposition values are given in the form of TEQs, it should be noted that neither emission nor deposition is equivalent to exposure or intake. Significant changes in composition can occur to complex mixtures of CDDs, CDFs, and PCBs as they move through the environment. Measurements at or near the point of human contact provide the best estimates of human exposure. TEQs are most relevant to potential for hazard and risk when they represent intake values. CDDs, CDFs, and PCBs have been found throughout the world in practically all media. This assessment proposes the hypothesis that the primary mechanism by which dioxin-like compounds enter the terrestrial food chain is by atmospheric deposition. Dioxin and related compounds enter the atmosphere directly through air emissions or indirectly, for example, through volatilization from land or water or from resuspension of particles. Deposition can occur directly onto soil or onto plant surfaces. Soil deposits can enter the food chain by direct ingestion (e.g. grazing animals, earth worms, fur preening by burrowing animals). Dioxin-like compounds in soil can become available to plants by volatilization and vapor absorption or particle resuspension and adherence to plant surfaces. In addition, dioxin-like compounds in soil can adsorb directly to underground portions of plants.

Support for this air-to-food hypothesis is provided by Hites [26] who concluded that "background environmental levels of dioxin-like compounds are caused by dioxin-like compounds entering the environment through the atmospheric pathway." His conclusion was based on demonstrations that the congener profiles in lake sediments could be linked to congener profiles of combustion sources. Further arguments supporting this hypothesis include: (1) numerous measurements show that emissions occur from multiple sources and deposition occurs in most areas, including remote locations; (2) atmospheric transport and deposition are the only mechanisms that could explain the widespread distribution of these compounds in soil; and (3) other mechanisms of uptake into food, for instance, from direct contamination or through packaging, are much less plausible. Direct uptake into food from soil or sediments is possible and could be important for "local" exposures. These routes are less likely to explain the general background level of dioxin and related compounds found in the diet of the general population.

The term "background" exposure has been used throughout this reassessment to describe exposure of the general population, who are not exposed to readily identifiable point sources of dioxin-like compounds, that results in widespread, low-level circulation of dioxin-like compounds in the environment. The primary route of this exposure is thought to be the food supply, and most of the dioxin-like compounds are thought to come from non-natural sources.

A background exposure level of 120 pg TEQ/day for the United States has been estimated [188]. These estimates are comparable to analogous estimates for European countries. These include estimates for Germany, which range from 79 pg TEQ/day based on Furst *et al.*[194] to 158 pg TEQ/day [28], 118-126 pg TEQ/day exposure through numerous routes in the Netherlands [29], and 140-290 pg TEQ/day for the typical Canadian exposed mainly through food ingestion [30]. It is generally concluded by these researchers that dietary intake is the primary pathway of human exposure to CDDs and CDFs. These investigators among others suggest that greater than 90 percent of human exposure occurs through the diet, with foods from animal origins being the predominant pathway.

Use of one-half of the detection level for nondetects is a reasonable but conservative approach to estimating low levels in samples. For some data sets, use of zero values for nondetects would result in significantly lower estimates. Setting nondetects equal to zero, however, does not significantly change the average TEQ levels estimated for most categories. In the current assessment, similar estimates of TEQs derived from different data sets, developed by different investigators in several countries, strengthen the probability that this inference represents the exposure of the general population in industrialized countries to dioxin and related compounds [31].

Levels of dioxin-like compounds found in human tissue/blood appear similar in Europe and North America. Schecter [32] compared levels of dioxin-like compounds found in blood among people from U.S. pooled samples (100 subjects) and Germany (85 subjects). Although mean levels of individual congeners differed by as much as a factor of two between the two populations, the total TEQ averaged 42 pg TEQ/g (42 ppt) in the German subjects and was 41 pg TEQ/g (41 ppt) in the pooled U.S. samples. These values do not include TEQs for PCBs.

New information on levels of dioxin-like compounds in human adipose tissue and blood has been published [33]. These measurements show that concentrations of dioxin-like PCBs can be more than an order of magnitude higher than concentrations of TCDD. Comparison with other published information suggests much higher levels of nondioxin-like congeners of PCBs and the possibility that concentrations of both types of congeners will depend heavily on previous human activities such as fish consumption. These data are consistent with the previous statement that dioxin-like PCBs may account for approximately one-third of the total TEQ in the general population.

The potential for formation of polychlorinated dibenzofurans (PCDFs) and dibenzo-*p*-dioxins (PCDDs) during thermal destruction of PCBs can be examined by thermochemical equilibrium calculations. The calculations predict that, under oxidizing conditions, formation of PCDFs and PCDDs is not thermodynamically favored. However, under pyrolytic conditions (absence or near absence of oxygen), as may arise in an inadequately designed or operated incinerator, thermochemical equilibrium calculations indicate that trace amounts of possible precursors to PCDFs and PCDDs can form [34].

The flame retardant chemicals' industry has historically been driven by regulations and standards. The normal fire-, smoke-, and toxicity-related standards have been joined by environmental standards caused by the alleged environmental impact of halogens and the alleged toxicity of antimony. Although suitable replacements have not been found for these materials in all cases, the environmental concern has served to depress their growth levels from what it would otherwise have been and/or channel the growth into alternative chemical products. In connection with the amendment of the Ordinance on Dangerous Substances, the federal government of German passed a new Ordinance on the ban and restriction of certain chemicals, compounds and products (Chemikalien-Verbots-Verordnung) which became effective on 1-st November 1993 (BGB1 I, 1720) and has been amended the first time on 6th July 1994 (BGBL I, 1493). The ordinance has replaced the following Ordinances:

1. An ordinance on the Ban of PCB and PCT of 1989
2. An ordinance on the Ban of Pentachlorophenol of 1989
3. First Ordinance on Chloroaliphates of 1991
4. An ordinance on "Dioxins" and "Furans"

In addition to Tetra- up to Hexachlorodibenzo-p-dioxins/furans with Chlorine atoms at position 2,3, 7, 8 (8 substances transferred from the Ordinance on Dangerous Substances, App. V, 3), the amendment of 6-th July 1994 extends the number of congeners of this type by some additional Penta- up to Octachlorodibenzo-p-dioxins/furans. Now the total number of restricted chlorinated PCDD/PCDF-Congeners amounts to 17 substances. The threshold concentrations for these chemicals in substances preparations and products were decreased considerably, depending on theirs toxic potentials. However, plant treatment agents, intermediates, and a few more products were excluded from this regulation. For the first time, 2, 3, 7, 8 - brominated dioxins and furans are restricted now as well; 8 PBDC/PBCF-Congeners were added to the list of the regulation. This was the result of an approximation process to the scientific progress concerning the appearance, environmental fate, toxicity and analytical methodology of these substances.

In December 1992, the European Commission granted Germany an exception under Article 100 (A) (4) of the treaty from EU-legislation issued in 1991 restricting the marketing and use of substances and preparations containing PCP and its compounds (Council Directive 91/173 EEC amending for the ninth time Directive 76/769/EEC). This consent was necessary because the German legislation imposed, differing from the EU-directive, wider restrictions and lower concentrations limits of PCP. After an action of France against the consent, in May 1994 the European Court of Justice annulled the decision by the Commission on the grounds that no adequate reasons had been given for it and thereby Article 190 of the treaty had been violated. In September 1994, the Commission pronounced a new decision and confirmed the German legislation again.

The Commission verifies now the possibility to propose a total ban of PCP for the EU. In this connection one can expect in a near future some new unexpected steps in this direction.

Several national regulatory bodies have implemented regulations on specific substances associated with flame-retardant applications.

In the European Community, the use of tris(2,3-dibromopropyl) phosphate (EC Directive 76/769/EEC) and tris(1-aziridinyl)phosphine oxide (EC Directive 83/264/EEC) in textiles has been banned. In 1977, the US Consumer Product Safety Commission banned the use of tris(2,3-dibromopropyl)phosphate in children's clothing [35].

The European Community has also banned the use of PBBs in textiles (EC Directive 83/264/EEC). Several countries have either taken or proposed regulatory actions on PBBs, as outlined in Table 6 [36].

Table 6. Country-specific actions on PBBs either taken or proposed [36]:

Country	Actions
Austria	Prohibits the manufacture, placing on the market, import and use of PBBs and products containing these substances.
Canada	Prohibits the manufacture, use, processing, offer for sale, selling or importation of PBBs for commercial, manufacturing or processing purposes.
Denmark	Implements EC Directive 89/677 banning the use of PBBs in textiles.
Finland	PBB may not be used in textile articles intended to come into contact with the skin (in accordance with EC Directive 83/264).
France	Implements EC Directive concerning PBBs and their use on textiles.
Netherlands	Proposed resolution would prohibit the storage of PBBs or products or preparations containing these substances or making them available to third parties. (Exports are excluded from the resolution).
Norway	Ban on PBBs in textiles intended to come into contact with skin, implementation of EC Directives76/769/EEC, 83/264 and 89/677.
Sweden	Ban on PBBs in textiles intended to come into contact with skin by implementation of EC Directive 76/769.
Switzerland	Prohibits manufacture, supply, import and use of PBBs and products containing these substances. Supply and import of capacitors and transformers containing PBBs is forbidden.
USA	No current production or use. Companies intending to resume manufacture must notify US EPA 90 days in advance for approval.

Controls on the emissions of dioxins and furans from municipal solid waste incinerators have been implemented in the United Kingdom under the Environmental Protection Act (1990). In Germany, a second modification of the Chemicals Prohibition Ordinance, which was adopted in 1994, imposes limits on 2,3,7,8-substituted chlorinated dioxins and furans and, for the first time, on some 2,3,7,8-substituted brominated dioxins and furans [36].

There are no regulations proposed or in effect anywhere around the world banning the use of brominated flame retardants. The proposed EU Directive on the brominated diphenyl oxides is withdrawn. Deca- and tetrabromo bis-phenol A as well as other brominated flame retardants meet the requirements of the German Ordinance regulating dioxin and furan content of products sold in Germany. The European search for a replacement for decabromo diphenyl oxide in HIPS has led to consideration of other bromoaromatics such as Saytex 8010 from Albemarle and a heat-stable chlorinated paraffin from ATOCH EM. The former product is more costly, and the latter, if sufficiently heat stable, lowers the heat distortion under the load (HDUL) significantly.

It doesn't necessarily mean the total ban of haloginated flame retardants in the next 5 - 10 years. But it actually means a complete reconsideration in a direction of polymers' flame retardancy development. It is obviously, the new efforts will be directed on the ecologically-friendly flame retardant systems.

REFERENCES

1. Pettigrew A. Halogenated flame retardants. In: *Kirk-Othmer encyclopedia of chemical technology*, 4th ed. New York, John Wiley & Sons, vol. 10, pp. 954-976, (1993).
2. Cullis C.F. Bromine compounds as flame retardants. In: *Proceedings of the International Conference on Fire Safety*, vol. 12, pp. 307-323, (1987).
3. Nelson GL (1995) Carbon monoxide and fire toxicity. Handout at the 6th Annual BCC Conference on Flame Retardancy: *"Recent Advances in Flame Retardancy of Polymeric Materials*, Stamford, Connecticut, May 1995, p. 16.
4. Babrauksas V., Harris R.H. Jr, Gann R.G., Levin B.C., Lee B.T., Peacock R.D., Paabo M., Twilley W, Yoklavich M.F., & Clark H.M., *Fire hazard comparison of fire-retarded and non-fire-retarded products*. Washington, DC, US Department of Commerce, National Bureau of Standards (NBS Special Publication No. 749). (1988).
5. Morikawa T, Okada T, Kajiwara M, Sato Y, & Tsuda Y., Toxicity of gases from full-scale room fires involving fire retardant contents. *J. Fire Sci*, **13**(1): 23-42, (1995).
6. Buser H.R., Brominated and brominated/chlorinated dibenzodioxins and dibenzofurans: potential environmental contaminants. *Chemosphere*, **16**(8-9), 1873-1876, (1987).
7. *IPCS Environmental health criteria 140: Polychlorinated biphenyls and terphenyls*, 2nd ed. Geneva, World Health Organization, International Programme on Chemical Safety, 692 pp. (1992).
8. *IPCS Environmental health criteria 152: Polybrominated biphenyls*. Geneva, World Health Organization, International Programme on Chemical Safety, 577 pp. (1994).
9. *IPCS Environmental health criteria 172: Tetrabromobisphenol-A and derivatives*. Geneva, World Health Organization, International Programme on Chemical Safety, 139 pp., (1995)

10. *IPCS Environmental health criteria: Polybrominated dibenzo-p-dioxins and dibenzofurans*. Geneva, World Health Organization, International Programme on Chemical Safety. 152.,pp, (1996).
11. Addink, R.; Olie, K *Mechanisms of formation and destruction of polychlorinated dibenzo-p-dioxins and dibenzofurans in heterogeneous systems*. Environ. Sci. Technol. 29: 1425-1435, (1995).
12. Ahling, B.; Lindskog, A. Emission of chlorinated organic substances from combustion. In: Hutzinger, O.; Safe, S., eds, *Chlorinated dioxins and related compounds, impact on the environment*. New York, NY: Pergamon Press.462 p, (1982).
13. Behrooz G.S.; Altwicker, E.R., Rapid formation of polychlorinated dioxins/furans during the heterogeneous combustion of 1,2-dichlorobenzene and 2,4-dichlorophenol. *Chemosphere* 32 (1):133-144., (1996).
14. Blumenstock, M.; Zimmermann, R, Schraumm, L-W; Kaune, A, Henkelmann, B, Kettrup, A. Presence of polychlorinated dibenzo-p-dioxins (PCDD), dibenzofurans (PCDFs), biphenyls (PCB), chlorinated benzenes (PCBz) and polycyclic aromatic hydrocarbons (PAH) under various combustion conditions in a post combustion chamber. *Organohalogen Compounds* 36:59-63, (1998).
15. Brominated FR Producers Make Universal Commitment: in *Fire and Flammability Bulletin*, p.2, November (1995).
16. *Dow Brand Dioxin*, ed. by J. Weinberg,, Washington, D.C., Greenpeace, September, pp. 34 pages, (1995).
17. Hardy M.L., *Regulatory Status And Environmental Properties of Brominated Flame Retardants Undergoing Risk Assessment In The EU: DBDPO, OBDPO, PeBDPO and HBCD*, 6th European Meeting on Fire Retardancy of Polymeric Materials, Lille, France, pp.15 September 24-26, (1997).
18. Norris R.et al., 1973, *Applied Polymer Symposium*, 22, p.195-219 (1973).
19. Pomerantz, I et al., 1978, *Health Perspectives*, 24, p 133-146, (1978).
20. Ahlborg U.G., Becking G.C., Birnbaum L.S., *et al*, *Chemosphere* **28** (6), 1049-1067 (1994).
21. U.S. Environmental Protection Agency, *Estimating Exposure to Dioxin-Like Compounds* EPA/600/6-88/005 Ca, Cb, Cc Washington DC (1994).
22. DeVito M.J., Maier W.E., Diliberto J.J. and Birnbaum L.S., *Fund. Appl. Toxicol.* **20**, 125-130 (1993).
23. U.S. Environmental Protection Agency, *EPA/600*, Vol 3 (1994).
24. Stehl R.H. *et al*, *The stability of Chlorinated Dioxins to Sunlight, Heat and Combustion*, In *Chlorodioxins - Origin and Fate*, E.C. Blair E.C. (Ed.), ACS series Vol. 120, p.119, Washington DC (1973).
25. Huang, H., Buekens, A. (1995) On the mechanisms of dioxin formation in combustionprocesses., *Chemosphere* 31 (9):4099-4117.
26. Hites, R.A. *Atmospheric transport and deposition of polychlorinated dibenzo-p-dioxins and dibenzofurans*. Prepared for the U.S. Environmental Protection Agency, Methods Research Branch, Atmospheric Research and Assessment Laboratory, Office of Research and Development, Research Triangle Park, NC., EPA/600/3-91/002 (1991).
27. Furst P., Furst C.and Groebel W., *Chemosphere* 20, (7-9), 787-792 (1990).

28. Beck H., Dross A., Ende, M. *et al. Ergebnisse von Ruckstandsuntersuchungen auf polychlorierte Dibenzofurane und Dibenzodioxine in Frauenmilch aus der Bundesrepublik Deutschland* Vol.34, Bundesgesundheitsblatt, pp. 564-568 (1991).
29. Theelen, R.M.C. Modeling of human exposure to TCDD and I-TEQ in the Netherlands: background and occupational. In: Gallo M., Scheuplein R.and Van der Heijden K. (Eds.) *Biological basis for risk assessment of dioxin and related compounds.* Banbury report No.35. Cold Springs Harbor Laboratory Press. Plainview, NY (1991).
30. Gilman, A.; Newhook, R. *Chemosphere* 23, 1661-1667 (1991).
31. Furst P., Furst L. and Widmers K., Body burden with PCDD and PCDF from food. In: Gallo M., Scheuplein R.and Van der Heijden K. (Eds.) *Biological basis for risk assessment of dioxin and related compounds.* Banbury report No. 35. Cold Springs Harbor Laboratory Press. Plainview, NY (1991).
32. Schecter A. Dioxins and related compounds in humans and the environment. In: Gallo M., Scheuplein R.and Van der Heijden K. (Eds.) *Biological basis for risk assessment of dioxin and related compounds.* Banbury report No. 35. Cold Springs Harbor Laboratory Press. Plainview, NY (1991).
33. Dewailly E., Ryan J.J., Laliberte, C., *et al*, *Environ. Health Perspect.* 102, 205-209 (1994).
34. Abbot B.D. and Birnbaum T.S., *Teratology* 43, 119-132 (1991).
35. *IPCS (1994b) Environmental health criteria 162: Brominated diphenyl ethers.* Geneva, World Health Organization, International Programme on Chemical Safety, 347 pp. IPCS (1995a) Environmental health criteria 172: Tetrabromobisphenol-A and derivatives. Geneva, World Health Organization, International Programme on Chemical Safety, 139 pp.
36. OECD (1994) Selected brominated flame retardants. Paris, Organisation for Economic Co-operation and Development, Environment Directorate, 152 pp (*Risk Reduction Monograph No. 3*).

Chapter 5

TRIBOCHEMICAL SYNTHESIS OF PYROMELLIT-AMIDOACIDS OLYGOMERS*

Vera A. Mit', Alexander P. Krasnov, Dina S. Kudasheva, Olga V. Afonicheva, Boris S. Lioznov, Irina I. Dubovik and Lidia I. Komarova

A.N. Nesmeyanov Institute of Organoelement Compounds, Russian Academy of Sciences, Vavilov Street 28, 119991, Moscow, Russian Federation

E-mail : *veramit@ineos.ac.ru*

ABSTRACT

The present work was devoted to the investigation of aromatic amine reactions under the conditions of non-traditional tribochemical synthesis at room temperature.

Oligomers of amidoacids based on diaminodiphenyloxide and pyromellite dianhydride have been obtained by in a different triboreactors. The products have been studied to elucidate the dependence of their properties upon synthesis conditions such as triboreactor type, presence of a dispersed medium, intensity and duration of mechanoactivation. Synthesis methodology has been developed and amidoacids oligomers of the molecular weight up to 2500 have been obtained.

Keywords. Oligomeric pyromellit-amidoacids, tribochemical synthesis, triboreactor, mechanoactivation.

INTRODUCTION

Investigation of the wide range of problems of mechanochemical synthesis of organic and inorganic compounds [1] revealed the perspectiveness of caring out the acylation reaction under the conditions of this synthesis [2]. It is well known that mechanoactivation of

---

* Acknowledgement: This work has been financially supported by the Russian Foundation for Basic Research (Grant № 01-03-32211).

monomers brings out two competitive processes: the growth of polymer chain and its destruction [3]. The aim of the present investigation was to separate those two processes to the maximum, so that it would be possible to determine optimum conditions for acylation of aromatic diamines.

The reactors used in this study were of the following types: first, a vibroreactor – eccentric vibromixer - which exhibits a complicated impact and friction activation of the reaction mixture, and the second, a shear micromixer – a device like a Bridgman anvil - which carries on the activation by means of intensive shear loadings. The latter one had been assembled in our laboratory for the purpose of this research and allows to control the applied load and rotation speed.

The possibility of reactions of migration copolymerization and preparation of Shiff bases in tribochemical reactors based on diamines was shown earlier [4].

EXPERIMENTAL

Materials

The starting materials for the synthesis of pyromellit-amidoacid oligomers (PAO) were diaminodiphenyloxide (DADPhO) and pyromellite dianhydride (PMDA). All applied reagents were analytical-grade commercial products.

While running a model experiment in the latter one DADPhO was acylated by phtalic anhydride (PhA). The benzoic acid was used as catalyst.

Apparatus

The synthesis was carried out in both vibroreactor and a shear micromixer.

A vibroreactor, eccentric vibromixer, is a 4-station model of ball-bearing sealed stainless steel milling jars. The weight ratio of balls to powder was 20:1. The jars vibrate with the amplitude of 5mm. This reactor employs a 2-way mechanoaction to grind rapidly by stroke and abrasion.

A shear micromixer is a setting similar to Bridgman's anvil and consists of two main parts: a rolling mortar bowl with a spiral rifling at the bottom and a coming down pestle cylinder with the opposite rifling at the face which gives loading pressure to investigating material. Those settings are assembled on the hydraulic press, which allows to vary the charge in a wide range of up to 50 kN and fixing speed from 1 to 60 rpm. The powdered material undergoes abrasion upon the intense shear force.

Measurement

Thermomechanical investigations were carried on the "Plastometer" device, with the plane indicator and loading of 50 g/cm^2 and constant temperature rising at a speed of 5 grad/min. The temperature gap was 30-380°C. The samples were obtained by a method of compression pressing at 500kg/cm^2 and room temperature.

The infrared spectra (IR) were registered on a UR-20 spectrophotometer in the interval of 400 - 4000 cm^{-1}. The samples of the powder compositions were prepared by pressing with KBr into tablets.

The quantitative analysis of IR-spectra for samples obtained upon different loadings was carried out applying the Beer-Lambert Law [5]. The relevant intensity of absorption band at 1640cm^{-1} typical for amidobonds, was determined by correlation to the band of benzene ring at 1020 cm^{-1}.

First, absorption of the standard was calculated:

$$\mathbf{D_{st}= lg\ I_{\lambda\ base}/\ I_{\lambda\ st},}$$

then absorption of investigated band

$$D_{\lambda}=lg\ I_{\lambda\ base}/\ I_{\lambda}$$

The intensity I_{λ} was measured at the top of the absorption peacks. After that the relative intensity was calculated as

$I= D_{\lambda}/D_{st}$ and expressed in percentage to maximum.

Mass-spectra of investigated samples were recorded on a Kratos-MS-30 spectrometer equipped with the system of data handling DS-50 and system of direct input of a sample into the ionization chamber at ionization energy 70 eV and amperage of 100 mkA.

Potentiometric titration of NH_2- and COOH- groups were performed on a digital pH-meter "Radelkis" OP-221/1 with a glass and calomel electrodes. The equivalent point was determined from the titration curve, built as a graph of U (mV) against V (ml).

Parameters of molecular-mass distribution (Mn) were determined by the method of Gel-Penetration Chromatography (GPCh).

The reaction mixture was washed form the catalyst by ethyl alcohol at room temperature.

Sol-gel analysis was performed in dimethylformamide (DMPhA) to calculate the percentage content of the sol and gel fractions.

Differential scanning calorimetry (DSC) was obtained on DSC-2 thermal analyzer in a sealed calorimetric bowls at a temperature scanning rate of 16 degree/min from 50 to 250oC. A sample weight did not exceed 10mg. Indium I10 was used as a standard.

Change of thermostability of oligomers at heating in dynamic regime in air (DTGA) was studied by usage of device Q-1500 D "MOM"("F.Paulik, J. Paulik, L.Erdey"). Rate of heating – 5 degree/min.

RESULTS AND DISCUSSION

The synthesis of PAO was carried out in vibromixer.

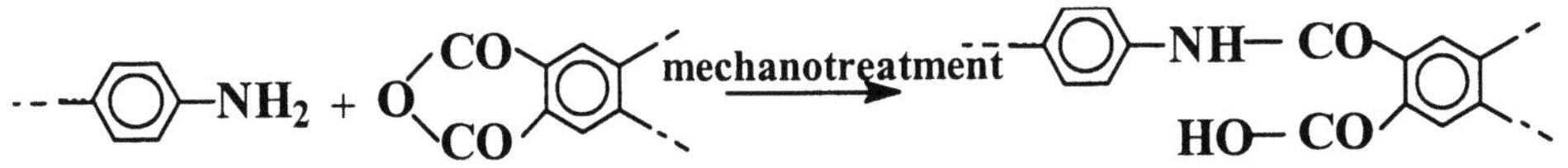

Scheme 1

While running the acylation reaction (Scheme 1) under the conditions of vibrotreatment it was observed, that mostly primary contacts of monomer interaction are taken pace, which leads to the synthesis of low molecular weight adducts of the following composition:

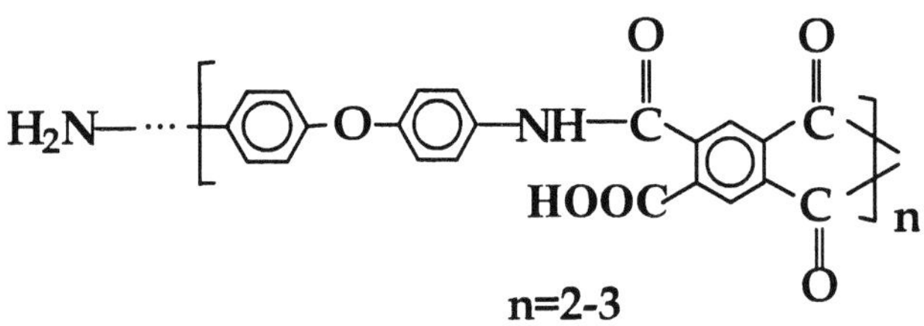

n=2-3

The properties of the products are listed in Table 1.

Table 1. The properties of pyromellit-amidoasid oligomers.

Molar relation PMDA/DADPhO		1:1.2	1:1
Content of NH_2-groups, wt %		2.0	5.5
Content of COOH- groups, wt %		20.0	18.0
M_n		600-1000	~600
Yield of non-soluble fraction, wt%			
without thermal treatment		100	100
after thermal treatment in air for 1 h	at 150°C	50	35
	at 200°C	8	10
Deformation* at 400°C, %		30	8
Loss in weight at 400°C (DTGA),%		6	3

* - the samples were obtained by means of compression at 500 kg/cm^2 and 200°C

The acylation reaction has been carried out under the conditions of a "dry" synthesis: at the absence of solvents in the reactor volume and presence of ethanol in the reaction mixture as a dispersed medium.

Thermomechanical properties of the obtained products are presented in Fig.1. It is shown, that in the case of the "dry" synthesis, thermomechanical curve (curve 2) indicates deformation of 4% in a low temperature region: form 50 to 100°C. This deformation then goes up to 16% at 250°C, probably due to some destruction of amidoacid fragments, which could take place under the "dry" vibrotreatment, as the acylation reaction is known to be reversible.

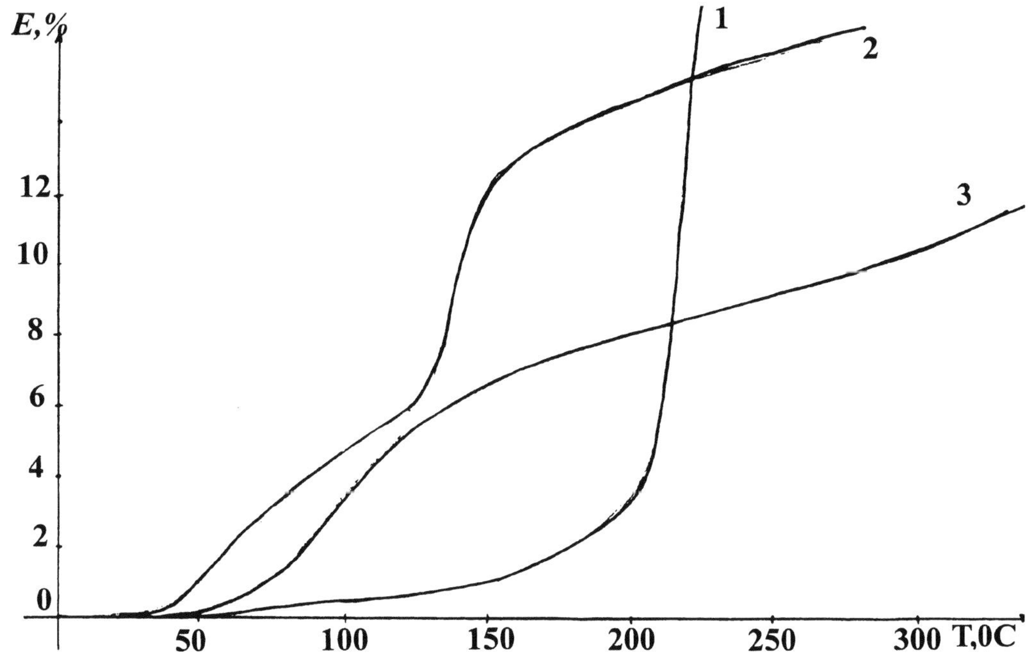

Fig.1. Thermomechanical curves of PAO samples: (1) initial mixture of monomers; (2) vibrotreatment in "dry" synthesis conditions; (3) vibrotreatment in ethanol.

Differential Scanning Calorimetry (DSC) was applied to analyze the initial mixture of DADPhO and PMDA (fig. 2, curve 1), as well as the product of the "dry" synthesis (curve 2) and the product obtained in the ethanol medium (curve 3). There were two peaks observed in the initial mixture under the experiment conditions: heating up to 250°C, with the maximums at 192 °C and 216 °C. Endothermic one at 192 °C corresponds to DADPhO melting, the second peak, most probably, demonstrates monomer interaction in DADPhO melting.

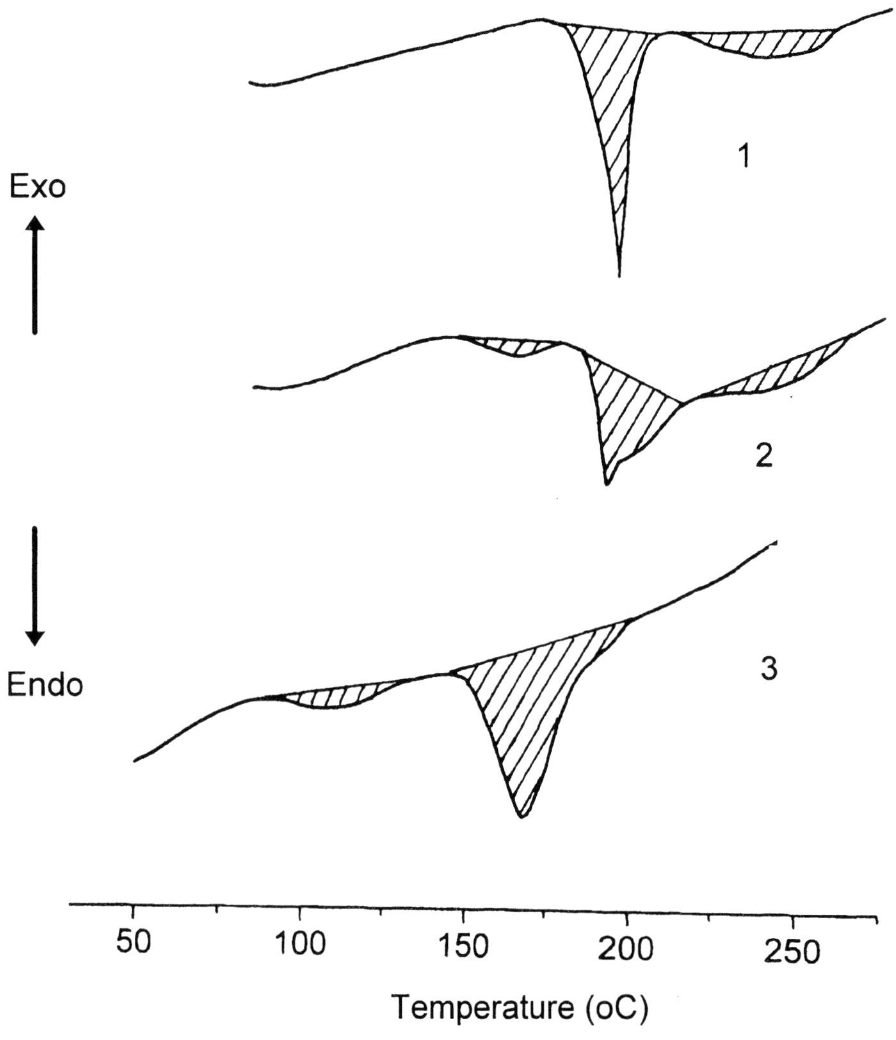

Fig.2. DSC-curves of PAO samples. (1) initial mixture; (2) "dry" synthesis; (3) synthesis in ethanol.

Two endothermic peaks of the PAO in the analyzed temperature region (synthesis in ethanol) correspond to a thermocyclization of amidoacid fragments. The cyclization is presented in Scheme 2. The first peak, which is less intensive, is at 117°C, the second one is at 167°C, which is in a good correlation with the earlier results of quantitative IR analysis [6].

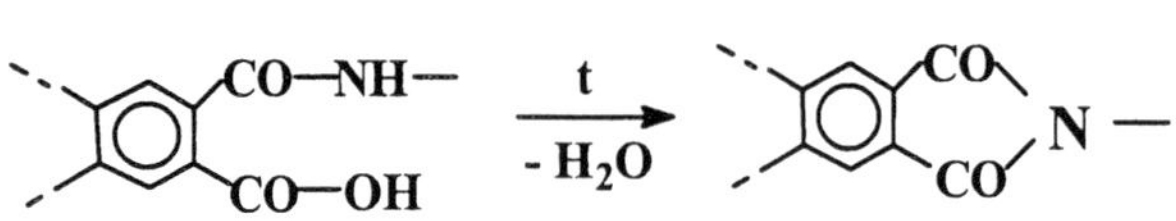

Scheme 2

Although the cyclodegratation begins at relatively low temperatures, it is known that the complete conversion of amidoacid fragments can be achieved only upon a prolong thermotreatment in the interval of 260-300°C [7].

DSC-curves of PAO sample obtained by a "dry" method (fig. 2, curve 2) are considerably different from those of a sample, obtained in ethanol medium. There is a peak at 216°C, the same as the one in the initial mixture, which characterizes monomer interaction in a melt. Whereas the first cyclization peak is getting shifted almost 50° up and has a slight heat effect, the second cyclization peak, in its turn, overlapped with the melting peak of unincorporated DADPhO with the maximum at 186°C. The above observations demonstrates that for the products of "dry" vibrosynthesis, the cyclization process, caused by thermotreatment, goes on less intensively than the one for products, obtained in a dispersed medium. The most possible explanation to that fact is the presence of unincorporated and destruction products in a reaction mixture.

It is clear that acylation and mechanodestruction processes are getting activated in air; it is then preferable to use a dispersed medium inside a reactor.

It was shown in literature [8] that polyamidoacids formation has an autocatalytic character due to the appearance of carboxylic groups after an anhydride cycle is getting opened. It was also described that this formation can be carried out under the conditions of a simultaneous loading of the initial mixture and benzoic acid as a catalyst.

In this research, we have studied the influence of benzoic acid as well: thermomechanical properties of the products, obtained in its presence, have been analyzed for both cases: for synthesis in ethanol and in "dry" medium.

The study revealed the fact that a considerable deformation of the samples synthesized in the ethanol medium begins at approaching of DADPhO melting temperature – 190°C. The thermomechanical curve of the sample synthesized upon "dry" conditions, has two main differences form the one described above: low temperature deformation is as small as 2%, starting at 50°C, which confirms the possibility of destruction processes, and the value of relative deformation on a plato in the interval 200-300°C is 2-2,5 times lower, which tells about the increasing of the sample's stiffness.

Functional analysis data are given in table 2, together with molecular-mass characteristics (Mn – number average molecular mass) of amidoacids oligomers, synthesized under different conditions.

Table 2. The dependence of pyromellit-amidoacid oligomers properties from synthesis conditions.

Properties	Synthesis conditions		
	without catalyst	catalyst – C_6H_5OH	
	in ethanol	in ethanol	"dry" synthesis
Content of COOH- groups, wt %	18.2	22.2	27.4
Mn	1200	2200	2500

It has been found out that an application of the catalyst resulted in the increase of carboxylic groups content from 18% to 27% comparing to the amidoacid, synthesised by a common method. Those data are in a good correlation with the results of calculation of the number-average molecular weight: the introduction of a catalyst into the reaction zone gives rise to the molecular weight up to 2200-2500.

The Synthesis of PAO Was Carried Out in Shear Micromixer

A model experiment has been carried out for a mixture of PhA and DADPhO (molar ratio - 2:1) for an investigating the possibility to perform the acylation reaction under the conditions of shear forces at low loadings.

Comparison of IR spectra of the initial mixture and the products has revealed the appearance of a band of strong intensity in a region of amide bond adsorption at 1640-1660 cm^{-1}. The estimating of molecular-mass characteristics have demonstrated that M_n of the obtained product is 400-500, which corresponds to the adduct of the following composition PhA-DADPhO and PhA-DADPhA-PhA.

At the next step a synthesis of amidoacids based on PMDA and DADPhO has been conducted inside a shear micromixer. The molecular-mass characteristics of samples, obtained under a variety of mechanotreatment conditions have been estimated (Table 3). It has been observed that in a first few minutes of mixing a rapid grow of polymer chain is taking place, and after 10 minutes the equilibrium is being reached. Longer shear forces (over 20min) lead to the decreasing of the number-average molecular weight, which is caused by the domination of amidoacid fragments' destruction over their formation.

Table 3. The dependence molecular mass from duration of mechanotreatment.

Type of triboreactor	Duration of mechanotreatment, min	M_n
Eccentric vibromixer Shear micromixer	3 10 20 30	900 1700 1850 1500

Thermomecanical properties of the samples obtained under different conditions have been carefully studied and it was shown that the increased duration of shear treatment gives rise to sample's stiffness. The appearance of deformation (3-4%) in the temperature region up to 100°C in products of the "dry" synthesis as well as in products of prolonged mechanotreatment, is an evidence of the presence of a low-molecular–weight fraction due to destruction processes.

Since one of the goals of this research was to synthesize oligomers of amidoacids, it was necessary to determining the limits of an allowed loading precisely, in order to prevent destructive processes. Thus, a quantitative analysis of the dependence of amid bonds content on the conditions of mechanotreatment has been performed.

The deepness of acylation conversion in a mixture of PMDA-DADPhO has been estimated by measuring the intensity of an adsorption band at 1620-1660 cm-1, typical for NH-CO- stretch of amidoacid fragment [9]. The IR-spectra are presented on the Fig.3. The essential increasing of absorption in the range of 1600-1700 cm^{-1} (spectra 2, 3) in comparison with initial mixture of monomers (spectra 1) indicative on active formation of amidoasid fragments in result of acylation reaction.

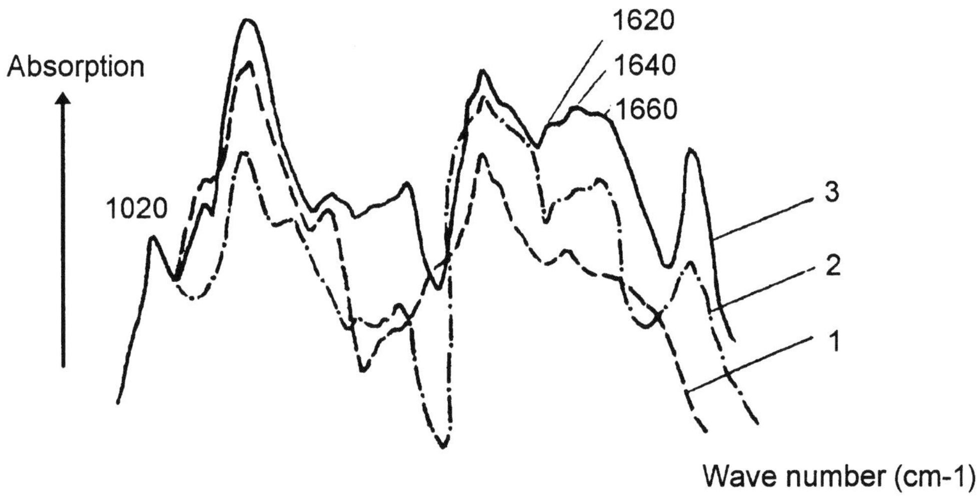

Fig. 3. IR-spectra of PAO samples (P= 0,5 кN, V= 30 rpm). (1) initial mixture; (2) 10 min; (3) 20 min.

It has been found out that amidoacids content in the reaction mixture depends to a great extend on the parameters of mechanotreatment. The results of the calculations are presented on Fig. 4.

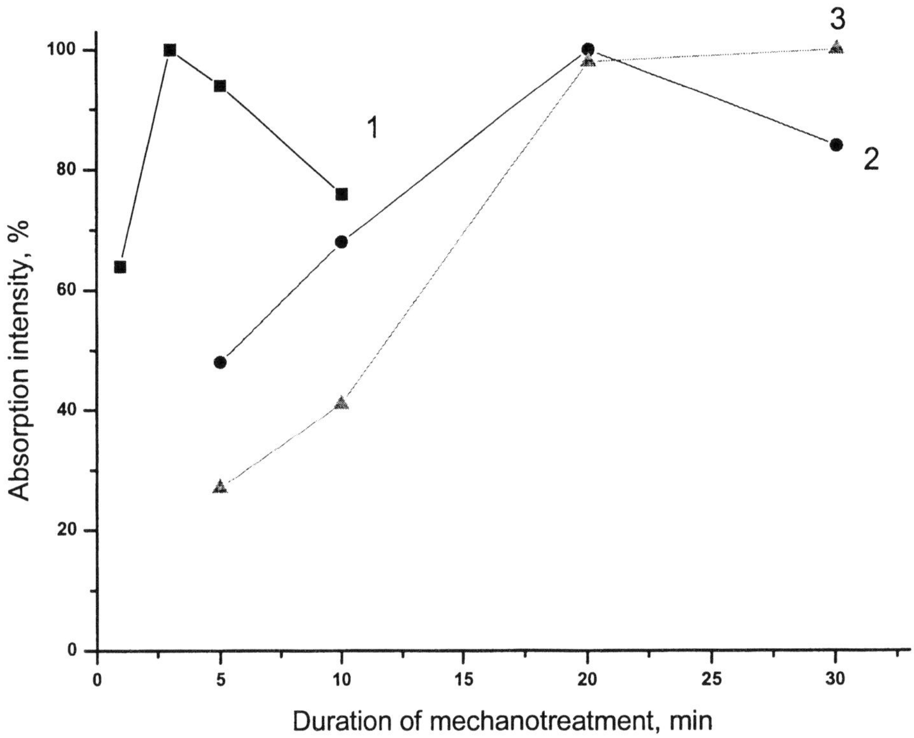

Fig. 4. The dependence of relative absorption intensity (*I*) of amido bonds (1640 cm^{-1}) from mechanosynthesis conditions:
(1) "dry" synthesis, P=1 кN, V= 30 rpm; (2) in ethanol, P= 0,5 кN, V= 30 rpm;
(3) "dry" synthesis, P=1 кN, V= 10 rpm.

Curve 1 characterizes samples of oligomer amidoacids, obtained by the method of "dry" synthesis at a loading of 1 kN. The optimal duration of a shear treatment corresponded to the adsorption maximum has been estimated to be 3 min at a speed of rotation 30 rpm. The increasing of the duration of the experiment leads to the developing of destruction processes and, as a result, the absorption intensity of amid bonds goes down. In the case of the synthesis in ethanol (curve 2) before 20 min a linear correlation is being observed between the yield of amidobonds and mechanotreatment duration. Wenn we changed the conditions of mechanotreatment - V = 10 rpm, those conditions allow the optimal running of the synthesis to be as long as 30 min. At the comparing of IR spectra of those samples it should be noticed that the sample obtained in ethanol has a stronger intensity of amidobonds adsorption.

Conclusions

The obtained results demonstrate that the acylation process runs intensively not only in eccentric vibromixer, as it was shown earlier, but in the proposed machine- micromixer of a shear type, as well. The methodology for a synthesis of amidoacids in the micromixer has been developed and the optimal experiment conditions have been determined. It has been demonstrated, that the use of ethanol as a dispersed medium allows minimizing a process of mechanodestruction of amidoacid fragments and achieved the formation of oligomer amidoacids with the molecular weight up to 2000.

The authors acknowledge Margarita M. Byzlanova and Irina V. Karandi for performing a functional group titration of the synthesized amidoacids.

REFERENCES

1. G. Heinicke, *Tribochemie,* Berlin, Akademie-Verlag, 1987.
2. V.P. Chuev, L.A. Lyaghina, E.Yu. Ivanov, and V.V. Boldyrev, *Sibirsky Khim. Zh.* **1**, 133 (1991).
3. N. K. Baramboym, M*ekhanokhimia vysokomolekularnyx soedineniy,* Kkimia, Moscow, 1978 (in Russian).
4. A. P. Krasnov, V. V. Kireev, V. A. Mit', D. S. Kudasheva, and L. I. Komarova, *High Perform. Polym.*, **12**, 395 (2000).
5. I.Kössler, *Methoden der Infrarot-spectroskopie in der Chemichen Analyse*, Akademische Verlagsgesellschaft GEECT&PORTIG, Leipzig, 1961.
6. A.P. Krasnov, V.A. Mit', L.S. Fedorova, L.I. Komarova, V.S. Papkov, L.Z.Rogovina, V.G Vasil'ev, M.M.Buzlanova, and I.V Karandi., *J. Polym. Sci. Part. A:Polym.Chem.* **39**, 391(1997).
7. M.I. Bessonov, M.M. Koton, V.V. Kudryavtsev, and L.A. Laius, *Polyimides – Thermally Stable Polymers*, Plenum, New York, 1987.
8. Ya. S. Vygodsky, V.A. Vasnev, S.V. Vinogradova, *Uspekhi Khimii*, **65**, 279 (1996).
9. J.G. Grasellii, and W.M. Ritchey, *Atlas of Spectral Data and Physical Constants of Organic Compounds*, **5**, Boca Raton, FL: Chemical Rubber Company, 1975.

Chapter 6

RELATIONSHIP BETWEEN THERMODYNAMICAL PARAMETERS OF ACTIVATED COMPLEXES AND INITIAL REACTANTS IN THE REACTION OF PEROXIDES WITH AMINES

A.A. Turovskiy[a], N.A. Turovskiy[b], V.I. Kopylets[c], E.A. Zagladko[d] and G.E. Zaikov[e]

[a] Pisarzhevskii Institute of Physical Chemistry, L'viv Department, Ukrainian Academy of Science, Naukova St., 3a, Lviv, 79601, Ukraine

[b] Donetsk State University, University St.,24, Donetsk, 34000, Ukraine

[c] Karpenko Physico-mechanical Institute, Ukrainian Academy of Science, Naukova St., 5, Lviv, 79601, Ukraine

[d] Commercial Academy, Samchuk St., 9, Lviv, 79000, Ukraine

[e] N.M. Emanuel Institute Biochemical Physics, Russian Academy of Sciences, Kosygina St.,4, Moscow,117977, Russia

ABSTRACT

The linear dependence between heats of formation and entropies of initial reactants on one hand and the correspoding thermodynamical parameters of activatrd complexes on other hand was obtained for the reaction of peroxides with amines. This relationship allows to estimate such parameters for another similar reactions of amines with peroxides.

Key words: activation energy, amines, enthalpy, entropy, peroxides

At present the mixtures of peroxides with amines as a class of reduction-oxidation systems are widely used for initiating the processes of radical polimerization. During the reaction between amines and peroxides free radicals are easily generated under low temperatures. Such radicals act as effective initiators through the interaction of anions with these free radicals. Reaction of chain growth termination in solution cage are then excluded before the desired degree of conversion. Sometimes during the choice of appropriative initiators a priori estimation of thermodynamical and kinetic parameters (without experiments) is possible on the base of structure analysis of reactants. We may apply quantum-chemical computatioanal methods to solve this problem. Ab initio approximations are effective for calculations of potential energy barriers of only small molecules. Application of semiempirical methods for examination of these barriers is not in general acceptible. So we propose a way of usefull estimation of thermodynamical and kinetic parameters of the reaction between amines and peroxides.

To determinate free activation energy ΔF^* one must add activation entropy ΔS^*, which is calculated by statistical methods with rough accuracy. Free activation energy of the reaction of peroxides with amines is determinated as follows:

$$\Delta F^* = \Sigma \Delta F_{b.c.} - \Sigma \Delta F_{b.r.} \quad (1)$$

where $\Sigma \Delta F_{b.c.}$ is a sum of free activation energy of the activated bonds in the activated complex, $\Sigma \Delta F_{b.r.}$ is a sum of free energy of bonds of the initial reactants, which are changed during the reaction. Taking into account that free energy

$$\Delta F_{r.} = \Sigma \Delta F_{b.r.} + \Sigma \Delta F_{b'.r'.} \quad (2)$$

wher $\Sigma \Delta F_{b'.r'.}$ is free bond energy (fixed both in reactants and activated complexes)

Then

$$\Delta F_{c.} = \Sigma \Delta F_{b.c.} + \Sigma \Delta F_{b'.r'.} \quad (3)$$

It is postulated that free activation energy of the activated complex is a linear function of free energy of reactants. Then accounting that ($\Delta F = \Delta H - T \Delta S$) we obtain next relationships $\Delta H_{c.} = \alpha \Delta F_r$ (Fig. 1) and $\Delta S_{c.} = \beta \Delta S_r$ (Fig. 2).

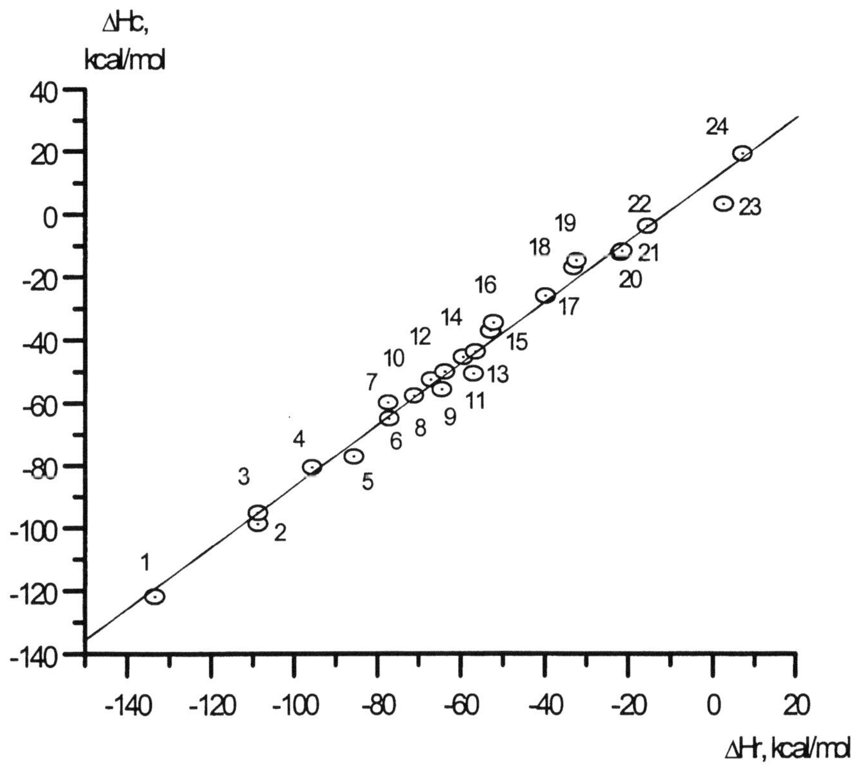

Fig.1. Dependance of values ΔHc on ΔSr for peroxide reaction with amine:
1 - p-CH_3O-PB + cyclo-C_4H_8NH 2 - PB + $(C_2H_5)_2NC\ H_2\ C\ H_2\ OH$ 3 - PB + $(C_2H_5)_2NC\ H_2\ CH(CH_3)OH$ 4 - PB + p- $CH_3\ C_6H_4N(CH_2\ \text{-}CH{=}C\ H_2)_2$ 5 - PB + $(n\text{-}C_4H_9)_2NH$ 6 - $C_6\ H_5C(CH_3)_2OOH$ + cyclo-OC_4H_8NH 7 - PB + $(C_2H_5)_2NC\ H_2\ C\ H\ (CH_3\ )OH$ 8 - PB + $(C_2H_5)_3N$ 9 - p-CH_3O-PB + $(C_6\ H_5)_2NH$ 10 - PB + $(C_2H_5)_2NH$ 11 - PB + cyclo-$C_5H_{10}NH$ 12 - $C_6\ H_5C(CH_3)_2OOH$ + $(C_2H_5)_3N$ 13 - PB + cyclo-C_4H_8NH 14 - PB + p- $CH_3\ C_6H_4N(CH_3)_2$ 15 - $C_6\ H_5C(CH_3)_2OOH$ + $(C_2H_5)_2N\ H$ 16 - $C_6\ H_5C(CH_3)_2OOH$ + cyclo-$C_5H_{10}NH$ 17 - $C_6\ H_5C(CH_3)_2OOH$ + $(C_2H_5)_3N$ 18 - $C_6\ H_5C(CH_3)_2OOH$ + $(C_2H_5)_2NH$ 19 - $C_6\ H_5C(CH_3)_2OOH$ + cyclo-$C_5H_{10}NH$ 20 - PB + $C_6H_5CH_2NH_2$ 21 - PB + $C_6H_5N(CH_3)_2$ 22 - PB + $C_6H_5NHCH_3$ 23 - p-NO_2-PB + $(C_6\ H_5)_2NH$ 24 - PB +$(C_6\ H_5)_2NH$

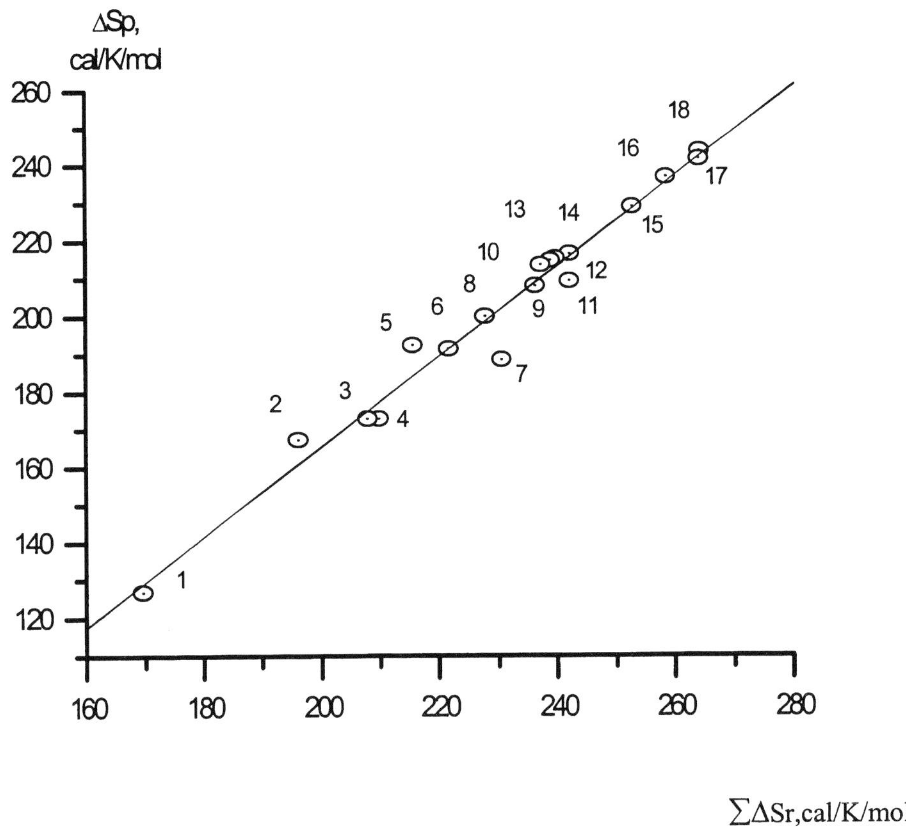

Fig.2. Dependance of values ΔSc on the summa of ΔSr for peroxide reaction with amine: 1 - $C_6H_5C(CH_3)_2OOH$ + cyclo-$C_5H_{10}NH$ 2 - $C_6H_5C(CH_3)_2OOH + (C_2H_5)_3N$ 3 - PB + cyclo-C_4H_8NH 4 - PB + cyclo-$C_5H_{10}NH$ 5 - $C_6H_5C(CH_3)_2OOH + (C_2H_5)_2NH$ 6 - $[C_6H_5C(O)O\text{-}]_2 + C_6H_5CH_2NH_2$ 7 - PB + $(C_2H_5)_3N$ 8 - [p-$CH_3C_6H_4C(O)O\text{-}]_2$ + cyclo-C_4H_8NH 9 - [p-$CH_3O\,C_6H_4C(O)O\text{-}]_2$ + cyclo-C_4H_8NH 10 - PB + $(C_2H_5)_2NCH_2CH_2OH$ 11 - PB + $(C_6H_5)_2NH$ 12 - PB + p-$CH_3C_6H_4N(CH_3)_2$ 13 - PB + $(C_2H_5)_2NCH_2C(CH_3)HOH$ 14 - PB + $(C_2H_5)_2NCH_2CH_2OH$ 15 - [p-Cl $C_6H_4C(O)O\text{-}]_2 + (C_6H_5)_2NH$ 16 - [p-$CH_3C_6H_4C(O)O\text{-}]_2 + (C_6H_5)_2NH$ 17 - PB + p-$CH_3C_6H_4N(CH_3)_2$ 18 - [p-$CH_3O\,C_6H_4C(O)O\text{-}]_2 + (C_6H_5)_2NH$

On the basis of experimental data on activation energies (E) and preexponents (A) for the reactions of amines with peroxides on one side and theoretical studies of their Δ Hc, Δ Sc, Δ Hr and Δ Sr on other side we can determine next values:

$\Delta H^* = E + RT$ (T=298 K)

$\Delta S^* = R\,[\ln A - \ln(kT/h)]$ (4)

$\Delta Hc = \Delta H^* + \Delta Hr.$

$\Delta Sc = \Delta S^* + \Delta Sr$ (5)

Values of Δ Hr and Δ Sr may be obtained in experiments as well. All our calculations were performed by PM3 method [1].

Our statistical treetments lead to the following equations with linear dependences:

$$\Delta \text{ Hc} = ((0{,}98 +(-)\ 0.02))\ \Delta \text{ Hr} + 11{,}44 +(-)\ 1{,}58 \qquad (6)$$
R=0,9937

$$\Delta \text{ Sc} = ((1{,}20 +(-)\ 0.05))\ \Delta \text{ Sr} + 74{,}57 +(-)\ 11{,}47 \qquad (7)$$
R=0,9754,

where R is a correlation coefficient.

If values of ΔHr and ΔSr are known for reactants, the values of ΔHc and ΔSc for the activated complex and its activation parametes are simply obtained as a difference between activated and initial states.

Experimental parameters of activation energies (E) and preexponents (ln A) were taken from the handbook [2].

REFERENCES

1. M.W.Schmidt, K.K.Baldridge, J.A. Boats et al (1993). *J.Comput. Chem.*, **14**, p.1347.
2. *Konstanty skorosti homoliticheskich zhydrofaznych reakcii.*(1971), Moskva, 'Nauka', p. 710.

Chapter 7

THE RELATIONSHIP BETWEEN THERMODYNAMICAL BEHAVIOURS OF ACTIVATED COMPLEXES AND INITIAL REACTANTS IN PEROXIDE DECAY REACTIONS

A.A. Turovskiy[a]***, N.A. Turovskiy***[b]***, V.I. Kopylets***[c]***,***
E.A. Zagladko[d] ***and G.A. Zaikov***[e]

[a]Pisarzhevskii Institute of Physical Chemistry, L'viv Department, Ukrainian Academy of Science, Naukova St., 3a, Lviv, 79601, Ukraine

[b]Donetsk State University, University St.,24, Donetsk, 34000, Ukkraine

[c] Karpenko Physico-mechanical Institute, Ukrainian Academy of Science, Naukova St., 5, Lviv, 79601, Ukraine

[d]Commercial Academy, Samchuk St., 9, Lviv, 79000, Ukraine

[e]Semenov Institute of Chemical Physics, Russian Academy of Sciences, Kosygina St.,4, Moscow,117977, Russia

ABSTRACT

The linear fit of the dependence of activated complex heats of formation, enthalpies and entropies on one side and starting reactants heats of formation, their enthalpies and entropies on the other side was found for the reaction of peroxide decomposition. This way of kinetical parameters estimation is allowed if values of ΔH and ΔS are known for starting reactants.

Peroxides are widely used as effective initiators in reactions of radical polimerization and vulcanization. In most cases thermal stability (free activation energy) can be estimated by means of computational methods. One of them to find activation enthalpies is an appropriate quantum-chemical approximation. Ab initio methods are not suitible for this purposes, because they require extremely huge amount of computer times even for molecules of middle sizes. However, we showed in [1] that an ab initio calculation for very small molecules, such as hydrogen peroxide, gave good coincidence with experiment for the reaction of its decomposition.

So one must attract semi-empirical methods to obtain results of thermodynamical calculations in short times. These methods seem to be very approximative in most cases of potential energy examinations. Thus, the decomposition of dimethylperoxide gives PM3 [2] activation energy barrier ca. 20 kcal/mole (Fig.1), whereas the experimental energy is much higher: ca. 37 kcal/mole.

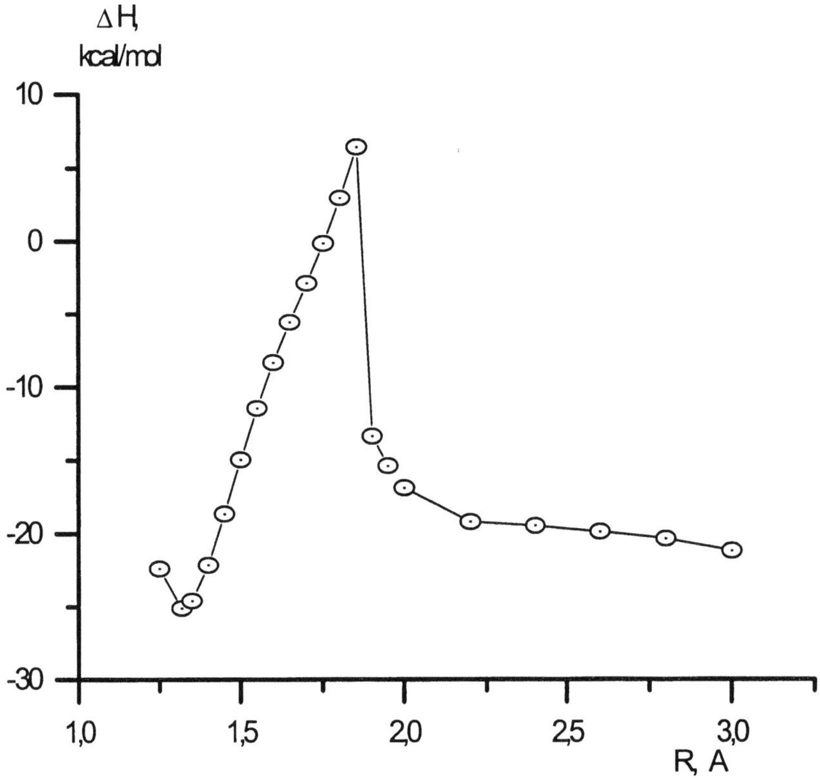

Fig.1. Heat of formation (a potential energy curve) of dimethyl per-oxide as a function of oxygen-oxygen distance.

Nevertheless semiempirical methods are sometimes used to estimate free activation energies ΔF^*. We propose a procedure of such estimation by a following equation:

$$\Delta F^* = \Sigma \Delta Fb.c. - \Sigma \Delta Fb.c. \qquad (1)$$

where $\Sigma \Delta$ Fb.c. is the sum of free energy in the activated bonds of an activated complex, $\Sigma \Delta$ Fb.r. - is the sum of free energy in the bonds of reactants, changed in the activation complex.

We found by PM3 calculations that energy of interatomic bonds are all changed for dimethylperoxide in the activated complex (Table 1).

Table 1. Bond energies (eV) for ground state of dimethylperoxide and its activated complex

bond	ground state	activated complex
O - O	-10,8245	-5,3833
C - O	-13.5521	-15,8524
C - H	-12.2436	-12,0651

In further calculations we widely use the values of heats of formation for initial states and activated complex instead of bond entalpies, which are changed during the decomposiotion of peroxides.

The free energy of a chemical composition formation Δ Fc and of a reactant Δ Fr is the sum of bond free energies:

$$\Delta Fc = \Sigma \Delta Fb.c. + \Sigma \Delta Fb'.c'. \qquad (2)$$

$$\Delta Fr = \Sigma \Delta Fb.r. + \Sigma \Delta Fb'.r'. \qquad (2')$$

where $\Sigma \Delta Fb'.c'.$ are bond free energies, with no changes during the process of peroxide decomposition. They are the same for reactants and activated complexes. The free activation energy of the reaction has next form:

$$\Delta F^* = \Delta Fc. - \Delta Fr \qquad (3)$$

Let's Δ Fc. is a linear function of Δ Fr. Then a similar dependence must be between Δ Hc. and Δ Hr ($\Delta Hc. = \alpha \Delta Fr$) (Fig. 2) and Δ Sc. and Δ Sr ($\Delta Sc. = \beta \Delta Sr$) (Fig. 3) as a consequence of the known equation:

$$\Delta F = \Delta H - T\Delta S.$$

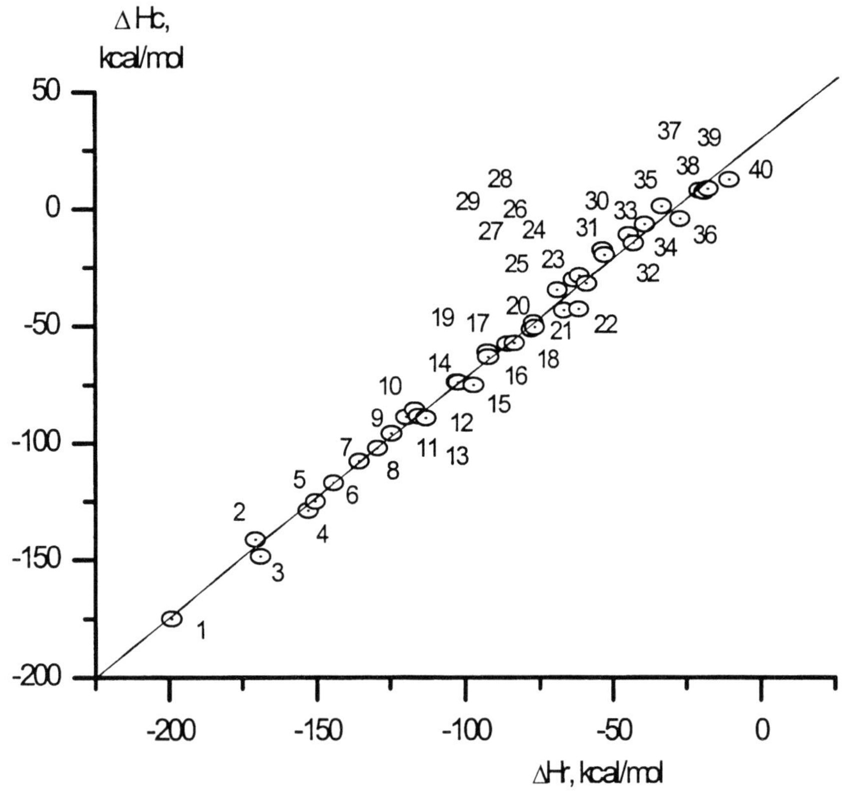

Fig.2. Dependance of values ΔHc on ΔHr for peroxides:
1 - $[C_2H_5O\text{-}C(O)O]_2$ 2 - t-butyl-C-OO-$(CH_2)_8$-C(O)OO-t-butyl 3 - phenyl-C(O)OO$(CH_2)_6$CHBrC(O)OOC(O)-phenyl 4 - $[(CH_3)_2CH\text{-}C(O)O\text{-}]_2$ 5 - t-butyl-OO-C(O)C(O)-t-butyl 6 - [n-C_4H_9-C(O)O-$]_2$ 7 - [n-C_3H_7-C(O)O-$]_2$ 8 - C_2H_5- C(O)OO- C(O)(n-C_3H_7) 9 - $[C_2H_5C(O)O]_2$ 10 - CH_3-C(O)OOC(O) C_2H_5 11 - $[CH_3\text{-}C(O)O\text{-}]_2$ 12 - [CH_3- CH_2 - C(O)O-$]_2$, 13 - t-butyl-C(O)OO-C$(C_2H_5)_3$ 14 - t-butyl-C(O)OO-t-butyl 15 - t-butyl-C(O)OO-t-butyl 6 - [cyclo-C_4H_7-C(O)O-$]_2$17 - C_2H_5C(O)OO-t-butyl 18 - Cl_3C-C(O)OO-t-butyl 19 - Cl- C(O)OO-t-butyl 20 - CH_3- C(O)OO-C(O)-phenyl-(o-OCH_3) 21 - CH_3-C(O)C(O)CH(CH_3)OOH 22 - ClCH_2- C(O)OO-C(O)-phenyl 23 - CH_3C(O)CH(OOH)$CH_3$24 - t-butyl-C(O)OO-phenyl(p-CH_3) 25 - [phenyl-$(CH_2)_2$-C(O)O-$]_2$ 26 - $CH_3(C_2H_5)$CHOOCH$(C_2H_5)CH_3$ 27 - CH_2=CH-C(O)OO-t-butyl 28 - t-butyl-OO-t-butyl 29-[cyclo-C_3H_5-C(O)O-$]_2$ 30 - $(CH_3)_2$CHOOCH$(CH_3)_2$ 31- phenyl-C(O)-OO-t-butyl 32 - C_2H_5OO C_2H_5 33 - [phenyl-C(O)O-$]_2$ 34 - cyclopenthene-OO-t-butyl 35 - CH_3OOCH_3 36 - t-butyl-C(O)OOCH(phenyl$)_2$ 37 - phenyl-$CH_2C(CH_3)_2$COOH 38 - [phenyl-CH= CH-C(O)O-$]_2$39 -[phenyl-CH= CH- CH_2-C(O)O-$]_2$ 40 - t-butyl-C(O)OOC(phenyl$)_3$

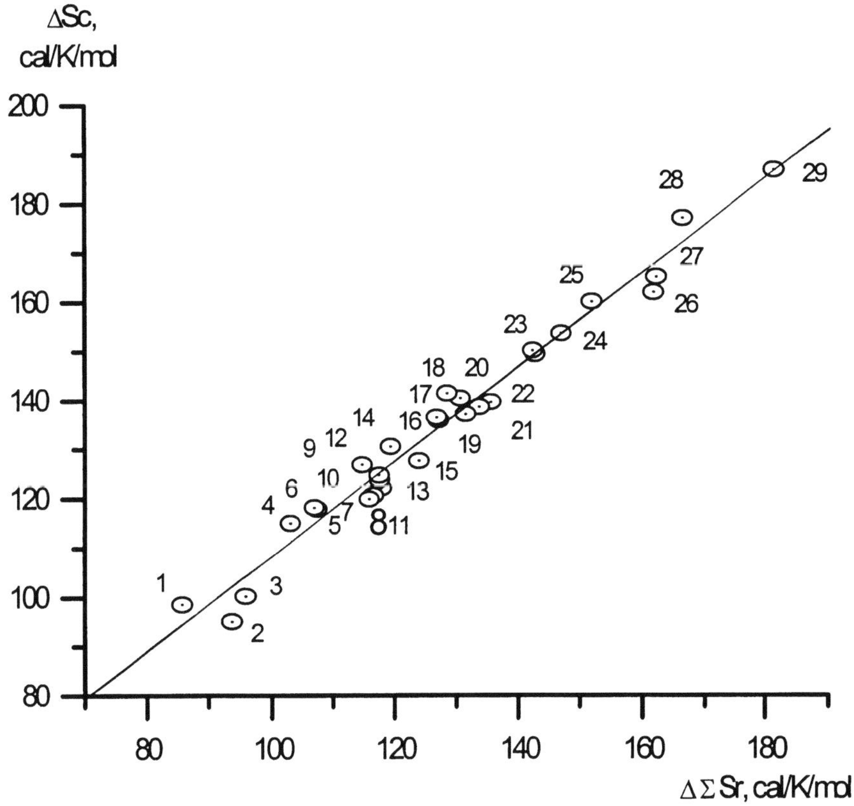

Fig.3. Dependance of values ΔSc on ΔSr for peroxides:
1 - t-butyl-C(O)OO-C(phenyl) 3 2 - [phenyl(CH2) 2- C(O)O-]2 3 - [phenyl-CH= CH-C(O)O-]2 4 - t-butyl-C(O)OO-CH(phenyl) 2 5 - (CH3) 3SiOOSi(CH3) 3 6 - [phenyl-(CH3) 2CO-]2 7 - phenyl- (CH3) 2C-C(O)O-t-butyl 8 - [n-butyl-C(O)O-]2 9 - phenyl-CH2-C(O)OO-t-butyl 10 - [n-C3H7-C(O)O] 2 11 - n-butyl- C(O)OO-t-butyl 12 - [t-butyl-C(O)O-]2 13 - [C2H5-C(O)O-]2 14 - Cl3C-C(O)O-t-butyl 15 - phenyl-C(O)O-t-butyl 16 -ClCH2C(O)OOC(O)CH2Cl 17 - C2H5-C(O)O-t-butyl 18 - ClCH2C(O)OOC(O)-phenyl 19 - C2H5C(O)OOC(O)(n-C3H7) 20 -[ethyl-C(O)O] 2 21 - [cyclo-C3H5-C(O)O-]2 22 - (CH3) 3COOC(CH3) 3 23 - ClCH2-C(O)O-t-butyl 24 - Cl- C(O)OO-t-butyl 25 - CH3C(O)OOC(O)CH3 26 - CH3C(O)OOC(O) C2H5 27 - C2H5OO C2H5 28 - CH3C(O)CHCH(OOH)CH3 29 - t-butyl-COOH

A great amout of experimental data on activation energies (E) and preexponents (A) for peroxide decay reactions and theoretical studies of their Δ Hc and Δ Sc allow us to determine next values:

$$\Delta H^* = E + RT \ (T=298\ K)$$

$$\Delta S^* = R\,[\ln A - \ln(kT/h)] \quad (4)$$

$$\Delta Hc = \Delta H^* + \Delta Hr$$

$$\Delta Sc = \Delta S^* + \Delta Sr \quad (5)$$

Statistical treatments lead to the following equations with linear dependences:

$$\Delta \text{ Hc} = ((1{,}03 +(-) 0.01)) \Delta \text{ Hr} + 30{,}83 +(-) 1{,}35 \qquad (6)$$

$$R=0{,}988$$

$$\Delta \text{ Sc} = ((0{,}963 +(-) 0.03)) \Delta \text{ Sr} + 11{,}96 +(-) 3{,}81 \qquad (7)$$

$$R=0{,}962$$

where R is a correlation coefficient.

Equations (6) and (7) may be used for estimation of Δ Hc and Δ Sc and moreover for determinations of activation parameters of peroxide decomposition reactions. The values of ΔHr and ΔSr are obrtained from experiments and by various computational quantum-chemical methods, the best of which is PM3.

Experimental parameters of kinitics of peroxide decompositions are taken from the handbook [3].

REFERENCES

1. 1.Turovskii, A.A., Turovskii, N.A. and Dolhushin M.D. (1976). *Doklady AN USSR*, **8**, p.724.
2. M.W.Schmidt, K.K.Baldridge, J.A. Boats et al (1993). *J.Comput. Chem.*, **14**, p.1347.
3. Konstanty skorosti homoliticheskich zhydrofaznych reakcii.(1971), Moskva, 'Nauka', p. 710.

Chapter 8

KINETIC FEATURES OF THE NON-ISOTHERMAL OXIDATIVE DEGRADATION OF EVA COPOLYMERS

L.V. Ruban, O.V. Sychugova, N.N. Kolesnikova and G.E. Zaikov

Institute of Biochemical Physics, Russia Academy of Sciences,
4 Kosygin Street, 117989 Moscow, Russia.

ABSTRACT

Thermogravimetric analysis was used for a comparative investigation of thermal-oxidative decomposition of EVA copolymers with a different vinyl acetate (VA) groups content. There are two stages of mass loss in this process. It was revealed that apparent activation energies are correlated with contents of VA-groups in EVA copolymers.

INTRODUCTION

We are investigated industrial EVA that was prepared by combined polymerization of ethylene with vinyl acetate in mass under high pressure. A broad utilization of EVA in industry caused by variety of useful properties these polymers. The content of VA-groups changes different properties EVA. The augmentation of VA-groups in EVA decrease hardness, heat resistance and crystallinity but increase density, elasticity, transparence and adhesion.

EVA is used in manufacturing different articles and details of technical application, in glue composition, as a pack-material, in medicine and etc.

In the present work we studied thermal-oxidative EVA decomposition by thermogravimetric analysis. Experiments were conducted in air on an MOM-Q-1500 D instrument (Hungary) at heating rate of 10° C/ min in interval 20-600° C. Initial weight of samples was 100 mg., and the mass loss (W) was determined.

RESULTS AND DISCUSSION

The detailed review of thermal-oxidative EVA decomposition was made in article [1]. In most cases thermal EVA decomposition was studied in vacuum or inert surroundings. Kinetic characteristics of these processes are listed in some articles. However the information on kinetic characteristics of thermal-oxidative EVA decomposition in a high temperature range is absent.

As the absorption of oxygen during thermal-oxidation EVA (200° C) is described by S-like curve and retarded by antioxidants [2] then that process has a radical chain mechanism.

EVA copolymers containing up to 30 % mass VA consists of blocks, which are built by 20 or more ethylene units and some VA units.[1] Therefore the initiation of EVA thermal oxidation is carried out as VA as ethylene blocks.

In article [1] was offered the next scheme of that mechanism:

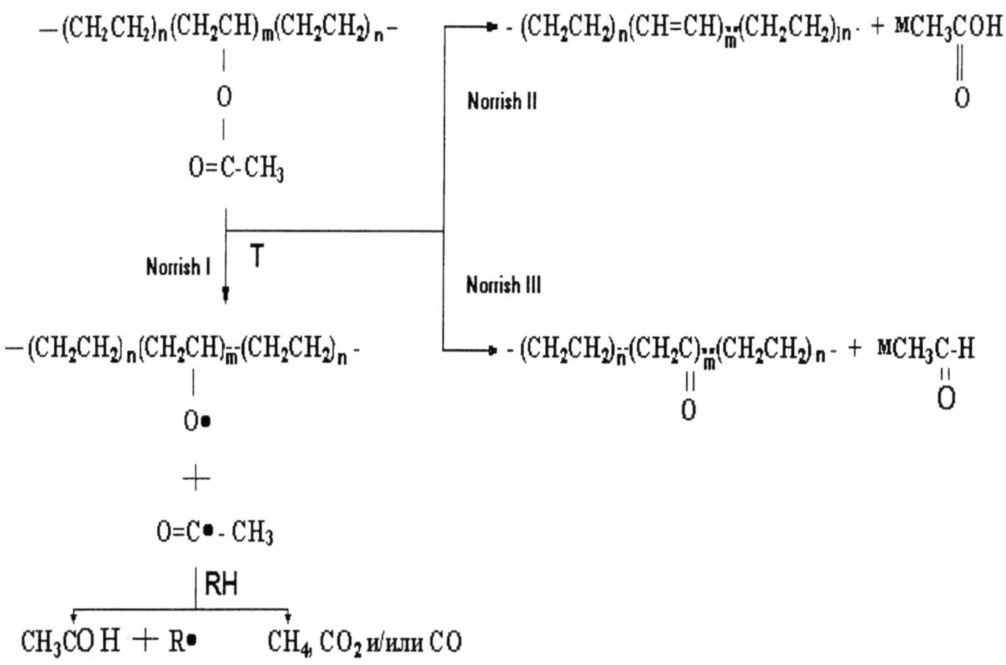

Products, received by reaction of II-type, may be also formed when the initiation of EVA thermal-oxidation is beginning on ethylene groups [2]. The oxidation occurs as an intramolecular process. Kinetic chain develops side ethylene block and retards on a carbon atom, which is bound with a VA-group.

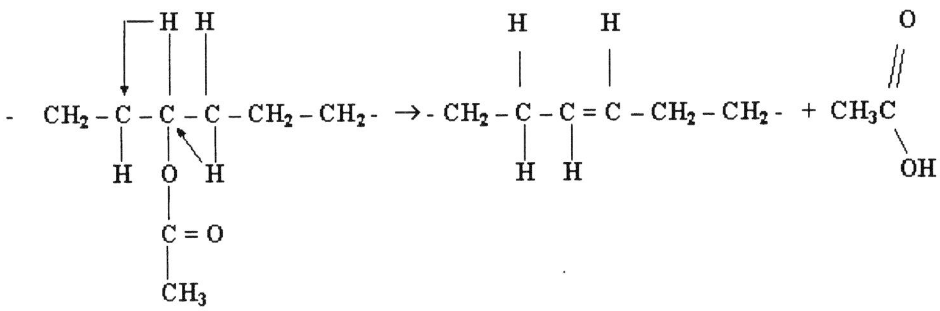

The thermodecomposition of EVA containing 43,8 % VA-groups was investigated by thermogravimetric analysis in inert surrounding at heating rates 5 - 40° C/min [3]. There were two stages of EVA thermodecomposition. An initial part concluded at 380-390° C. A main product in that reaction stage was acetic acid. Irrespective of heating rates the average weight loss (ΔW %) for first stage of 11 runs was ~30 % of a initial sample mass. The TG-curve was processed using the Coats-Redfern integral method [4]. The initial part of the TG-curve for first stage indicates the induced period of the non-isothermal decomposition. The upward trend of the last part overlaps with the beginning of the second degradation stage, which has another activation energy. These two parts of the curves were neglected in the data processing.

The experimental TG-curve transformed as $log\ [-ln\ (1 - \alpha)/T^2]$ vs. T^{-1}, where α is the reaction fraction. This implied that the thermal EVA degradation was a first-order reaction [5]. The slopes obtained from the principal part of the mass loss give the E_a (=2,303 R · slope).

We also accepted the Coats-Redfern integral method and the assumption on first - order reaction in our investigation of thermal-oxidative EVA decomposition.

The typical TG-curve for the non-isothermal oxidative EVA decomposition is presented in Fig. 1. The two-stage process of degradation observed for all EVA samples with different VA-groups content. The first stage completed about 380° C and the next proceeded in the interval 380-510° C. The initial and transitional ranges of curve were neglected because of the above-mentioned reasons. The plot of $log\ [-ln\ (1 - \alpha)/T^2]$ vs. T^{-1} for typical TG-data at a heating rate of 10° C/min is shown in Fig. 2. It is obvious clear from Fig 2 a non-isothermal oxidative EVA degradation was proceeding by two consecutive mechanisms with different apparent activation energies. It is characteristically that apparent activation energy of low-temperature stage decreased but high-temperature stage increased if numbers of VA-groups in EVA copolymer are raised.

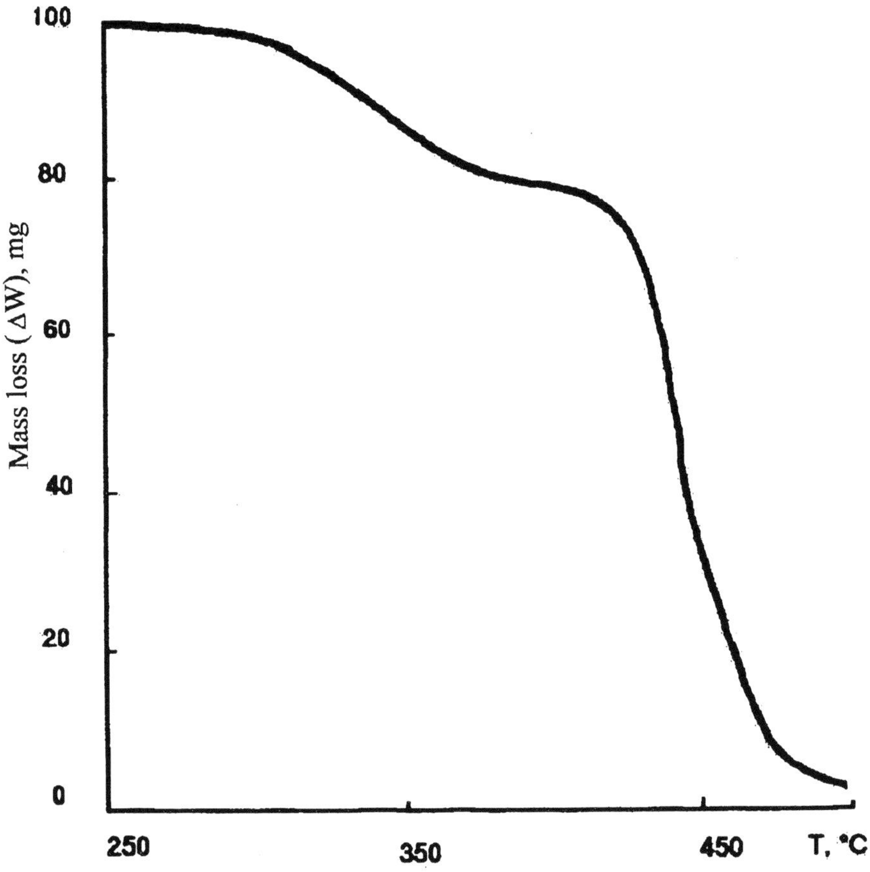

Figure 1. Mass loss (TG) curve of thermal-oxidative EVA decomposition with VA-groups content 26 mass.%.

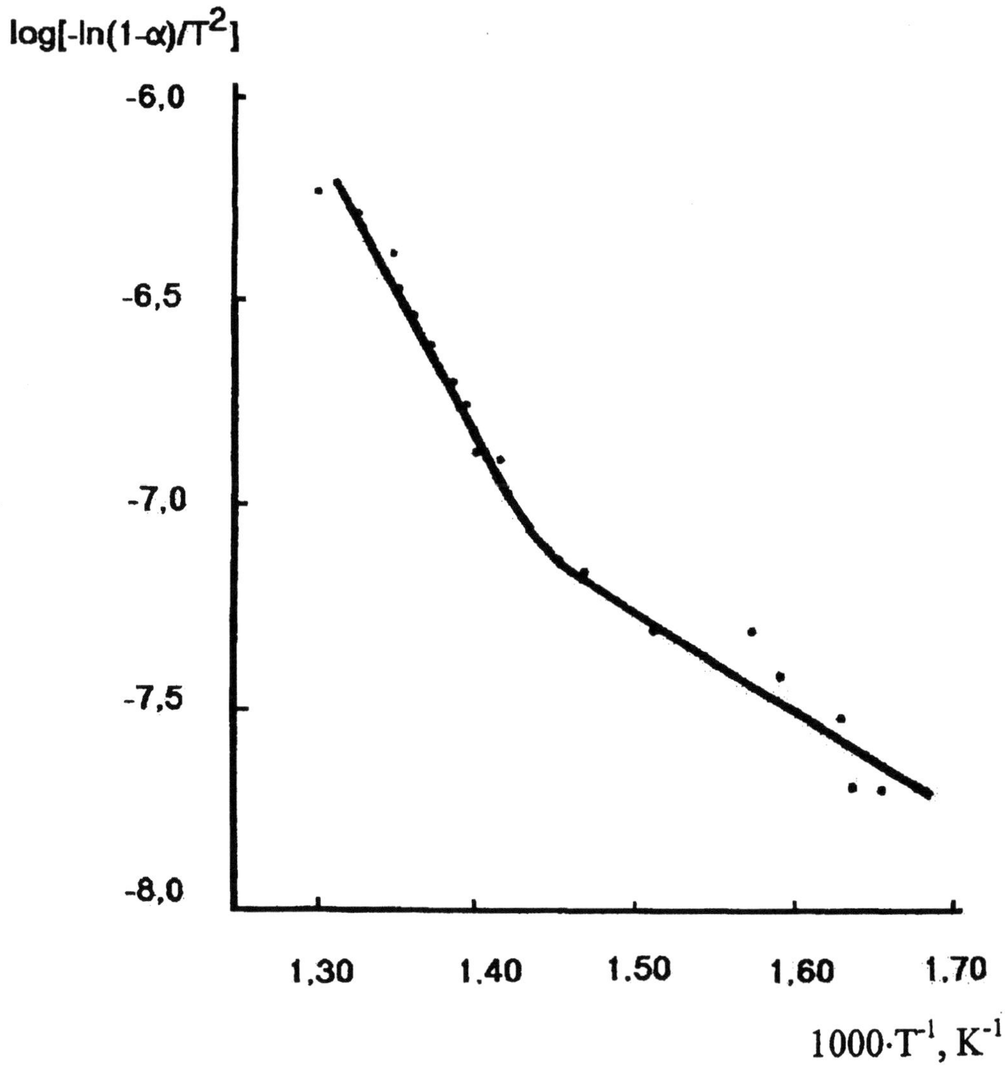

Figure 2. Transformed TG-curve for EVA with VA-groups content 26 mass. %.

The interdependency calculation values of apparent activation energies for two-stages of thermal-oxidative EVA decomposition and VA-groups content is shown on Fig. 3 and Fig.4 accordingly.

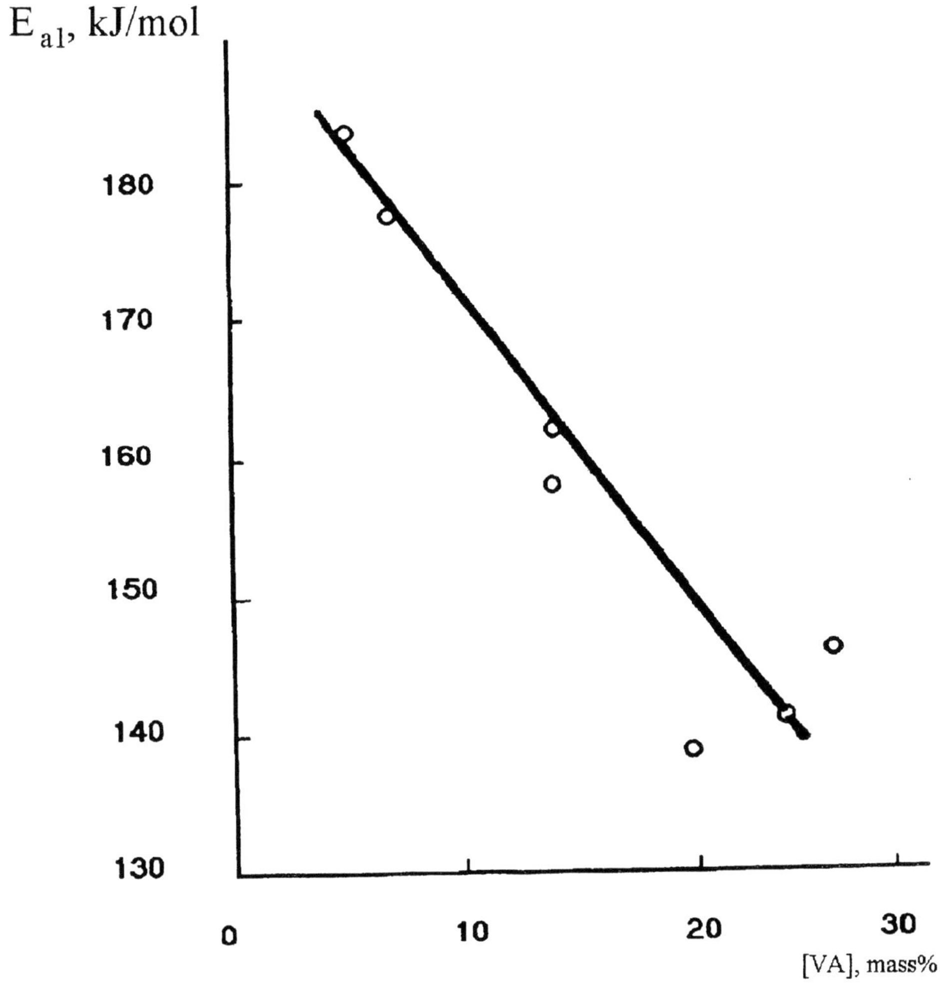

Figure 3. The influence of VA-groups content on apparent activation energy for first stagy of EVA decomposition.

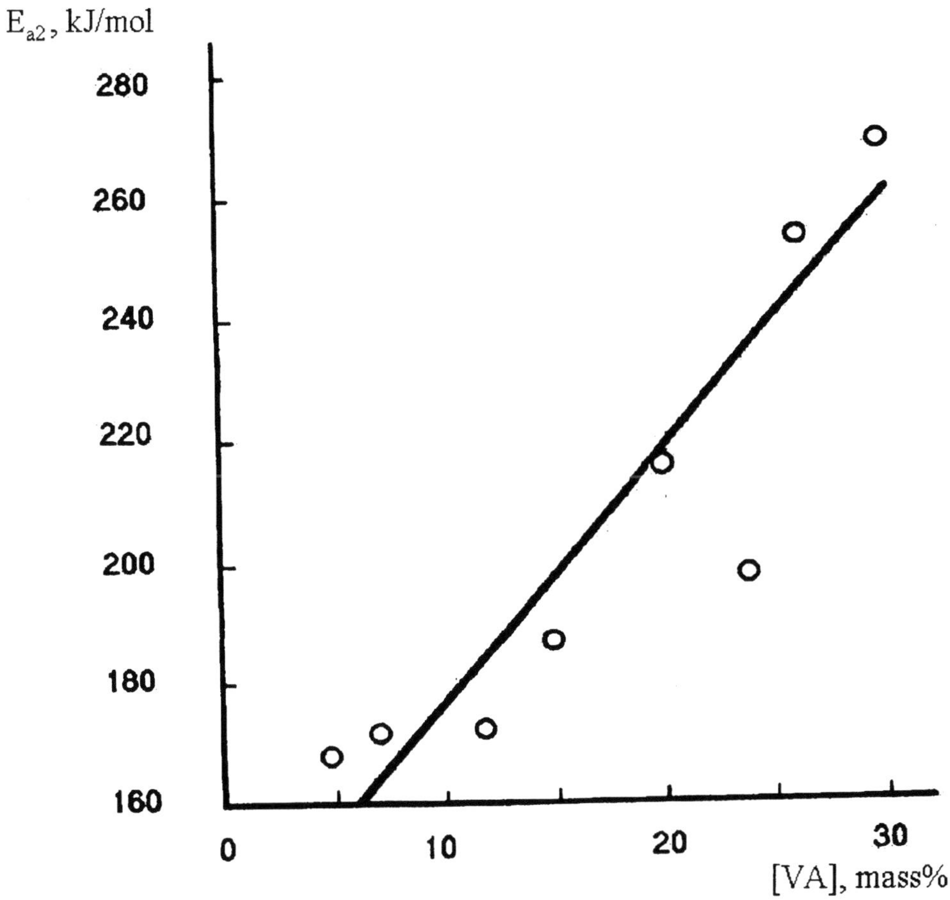

Figure 4. The influence of VA-groups content on apparent activation energy for second stage of EVA decomposition.

These dependencies described by following correlative linear equations:

$E_{a\,1}$ = - 2.06 [VA%] + 191.0 kJ/mol, k =0.98 (1)

$E_{a\,2}$ = 4.02 [VA%] + 136.1 kJ/mol, k=0.84 (2)

where [VA%] –VA-groups content in the sample in mass %, k – correlative coefficient.

On the first stage process if VA-groups content increases then EVA thermal-oxidative stability decreases. That phenomenon is connected as with extension of VA-blocks dimensions so catalytic action of educed acetic acid. The values of the apparent activation energies of thermal-oxidative EVA decomposition received by us are considerably less than those received under the thermal decomposition in vacuum or inert surroundings. [3].

We suppose that net structures forms under macroradical recombination in the process thermal-oxidative EVA decomposition.

The destruction of the polymeric chains occurs in the second part of thermal-oxidative EVA decomposition. The more VA-group content in EVA molecule the more branched second oxidation products produced in initial reaction stage. Therefore the apparent activation energy of thermal-oxidative EVA decomposition in the secondary stage is greater than those in the first stage of the decomposition. The correlative equation (2) agrees with supposed interpretation of two-stage passage of thermal-oxidative EVA decomposition.

On later we will attend to study an intermediate and final reaction products. It will permit to recognize thermal-oxidative EVA decomposition mechanism in detail.

REFERENCES

1. Czanderna A.W., Pern F.G. //*Solar Energy Materials and Solar Cells*.1996.v. 43. p. 101.
2. Lugova L.I., Popova G.S., Pozdnjkova F.O. //*Vysokomolek.Soed.* B. 1976. v. 17. N. 8. p. 91.
3. Cai X.E., Shen H.//*J.Therm.Anal.and Calorimetry*. 1999. v. 55. p.67.
4. Coats A.W., Redfern J.P. //*J.Polym.Sci. (Polymer Letters)*. 1965. v. 3. N. 11. p. 917.
5. Marin M.L., Jimenez A., Lopez J., Vilaplana J. //*J. Thermal Anal.* 1996. v. 47. p. 247.

Chapter 9

KINETICS OF GROWTH OF THE BACTERIAL STRAIN RHODOCOCCUS LUTEUS AC-1169 ON DIFFERENT SUBSTRATE

R.I. Vildanova-Martsishin*, A.A. Turovsky* and G.E. Zaikov**

*Department of Physical Chemistry and Technology of Fossil Fuels,
Institute of Physical Chemistry, National Academy of Sciences of Ukraine,
Naukova Str., 3a, UA-79052, L'viv, Ukraine, e-mail: mrs@inbox.ru

**N.M. Emanuel Institute Biochemical Physics, Russian Academy of Sciences,
4 Kosygin Street, Moscow, 117334, Russia

ABSTRACT

As a result of wide selection the most perspective culture Rhodococcus luteus BKM Ac-1169 is selected. The biosurfactant is a surface-active glycolipid produced during the stationary growth phase of Rhodococcus luteus Ac-1169 on n-hexadecane and saccharose in conditions of aeration. The kinetics of growth of culture and synthesis of biosurfactant with determination of specific growth rate (μ), max specific growth rate (μ_{max}), constant of affinity the cell to substrate (K_s) is study. The mechanism of inhibition of the process of growth of culture of Rhodococcus luteus and biosurfactant production is made out. The periods of induction on kinetic curve of growth microbial of population are defined.

Key words: biosurfactant, glycolipids, Rhodococcus luteus, kinetics, specific growth rate, maximum specific growth rate, constant of affinity the cell to substrate, *lag*-phase, period of induction.

INTRODUCTION

Main modern direction of study of biosurfactant – substitute synthetic surfactant (having lower biodegradability, higher toxicity, ecologically dangerous, calling allergic reacting and in a number of cases being cancerogen) on biosyrfactants (having lower toxicity, higher biodegradability, high selectivity and specific activity at extreme temperatures, pH and salinity). Besides there is also social-political aspect of a problem coupled to necessity of decision of power (production, transport and petroleum refining), medical (creating of the new medical drugs on a basis of biosurfactant) and other questions.

Among the main tendencies of study biosurfactant it is necessary to dedicate following: search cheap substrates on the basis of industrial, municipal and agricultural waste products; engineering of new high-performance know-hows of extraction and clearing biosurfactants; applying bacteria and biosurfactants for enhanced oil recovery; clearing of an environment from oil pollution; transport granulated black coal on pipe lines and others.

Biosurfactants are surface-active agents produced by bacteria, yeast and fungi and include such products as phospholipids, lipopeptides, glycolipids, lipopolysaccharides and fatty acids. From the literature, it is know that the bacteria from the genus *Rhodococcus* are capable of producing effective surfactants. The strain *Rhodococcus luteus VKM Ac-1169* is the most perspective culture between members of the "rhodochrous" group of bacteria. In particular, *Rhodococcus luteus* produced glycolipid biosurfactants when grown on hydrocarbons and saccharose in batch culture. We describe the kinetics of growth and biosurfactant synthesis by Rhodococcus luteus. The criterions for a rating of researched cultures were surface and interfacial tension, ability to forming microemulsion (the emulsifying activity $-E_{24}$ – of its culture broth). . The strain *Rhodococcus luteus VKM Ac-1169* is capable to synthesis extracellular glycolipids lowering surface (σ_s) and interfacial (σ_i) tension of its culture broth to 27,6 mN/m and 2,7 mN/m according; having high emulsifying activity - $E_{24} = 50\%$.

The main aim this work described here was the research of growth the strain *Rhodococcus luteus* and synthesis of biosurfactant during the stationary growth phase on *n*-hexadecane and saccharose in conditions of aeration. The specific growth rate (μ), the maximum specific growth rate (μ_{max}), constant of affinity the cell to substrate (Ks) has been determined. Thus for accounts of these parameters of growth the formal methods applied at analysis of kinetic regularities of fermentation catalysis were used [5].

MATERIALS AND METHODS

Rhodococcus luteus was grown in 500-ml conical flasks containing 100 ml of a sterile medium at a pH value of 7,0. The culture was maintained at 30°C on a reciprocating shaker at 200 rev/min for 312 hours [6,7]. As a sources of carbon and energy used *n*-hexadecane and saccharose. Each litre of mineral salts medium contained (g/l): $K_2HPO_4*3H_2O$ - 2,0; KH_2PO_4-1,2; $NaNO_3$-3,0; $MgSO_4*7H_2O$ - 0,5; citrate Na - 5,0; $FeSO_4*7H_2O$ - 0,0005; $CaCl_2*3H_2O$ - 0,05; the solution of microelements - 1 ml. A yeasty extract ("Difco") added in concentration 1,0 g/l. The solution of microelements contained (g/l): EDTA - 1,0; $MnSO_4$-3,0; $FeSO_4$-0,1; $CaCl_2*2H_2O$ - 0,1; $CoCl_2$-0,1; $ZnSO_4$-0,1; $CuSO_4$-0,01; $Al(SO_4)_2$-0,01; H_3BO_3-0,01; $Na_2Mo_4*2H_2O$ - 0,01; the distilled water - up to 1 l.

After cultivation, the cells were separated by centrifugation at 8000 rev/min during 20 min, dried at 105°C and weighed. Extraction of lipids from the supernatant carried out on a method [6], their separation – a method TLC on HPTLC – on silica gel G-60 thin-layer plates ("Merck", Germany). For separation lipids used such systems of solvents: chloroform-methanol-acetone-acetic acid (90:10:6:1) - for polar lipids; hexane-diethyl ether - acetic acid (90:10:1) - for nonpolar lipids. Lipids were visualised by 5 % alcoholic solution phosphomolybdic acid and vapours of iodine [9]; glycolipids – anthrone reagent and anisaldehyde [9,10]; peptide-lipids - 1 % solution ninhydrin in alcohol and benzidine reagent [9,10]. Trehalose dimycolic acid, trehalose monomycolic acid used as a standard.

For measurements of the surface (σ_s) and interfacial (σ_i) tensions was used the Wilhelmy method with a platinum plate [11]. Emulsifying activity defined on a method [12] in our modification: 10 ml of culture broth and 10 ml of liquid paraffines (C_{12}-C_{14}) mixed during 2 minutes on a homogenizer "Mu-2". The obtained mixture carries to a gaging test-tube NS-14 (GDR). Measuring of values of index of emulsification (E_{24}) carry out in 24 hours as the ratio of altitude of an emulsive layer to communal altitude of fluid in a gaging test-tube and expressed in percentage.

Results and Discussion

Feature of kinetics of microbial population is the dependence of specific growth rate of culture from concentration limiting substrate. Is learnt the capacity of culture of bacteria *Rhodococcus luteus VKM Ac-1169* to growth on the mineral salts medium and to synthesis of biosurfactant depending on concentration of a source of carbon (*n*-hexadecane and saccharose) (Tab. 1).

Table 1. The dependence of accumulation of biomass and biosurfactants at growth the strain *Rhodococcus luteus* on the mineral salts medium with different concentrations a sources of carbon and energy

Substrate, % /Vol	Biomass (M_{max}), g/l		Trehalose lipids (L_{max}), g/l	
	saccharose	*n*-hexadecane	saccharose	*n*-hexadecane
0,5	4,113	2,384	0,05	0,2
1	5,405	3,65	0,076	0,22
1,5	9,033	4,883	0,086	0,383
2	12,58	4,903	0,15	0,62
2,5	12,589	5,044	0,5	1,02
3	12,599	5,4	0,51	1,5
3,5	12,671	6,264	0,52	1,85
4	12,76	6,32	0,53	1,9
5	13,48	6,75	0,55	1,95
7	12,03	7,7	0,6	2,05
10	11,22	8,515	0,7	2,03

Is detected that the culture *Rhodococcus luteus* at growth on saccharose gives greatest biomass (12-13 g/l) in comparison with growth on *n*-hexadecane (6-8,5 g/l). However, at growth on saccharose the yield of the surface-active product – minimum (0,5 g/l), and at growth on *n*-hexadecane – four times is more (2 g/l). As has shown study of surface-active and emulsifying properties of culture broth (Tab. 2) – the surface tension (σ_s) with increase of concentration substrate is a gradually decreased: on saccharose - from 49,7 to 29,6 mN/m, on *n*-hexadecane - from 44,9 to 27,4 mN/m.

Table 2. The dependence of index of emulsification ($_{24}$) and the surface tension (σ_s) from concentration substrate

Substrate, %/Vol	σ_s, mN/m		E_{24}, %	
	saccharose	*n*-hexadecane	saccharose	*n*-hexadecane
0,5	49,7	44,9	0	0
1	47,3	32,3	0	0
1,5	43,5	29,9	0	5
2	31,3	30,4	10	45
2,5	31,3	29	10	50
3	30,8	28,5	10	50
3,5	29,6	28,5	10	50
4	29,6	28,5	10	50
5	29,6	27,4	10	50
7	29,6	27,4	10	50
10	29,6	27,4	10	50

The emulsification of hydrocarbons by culture broth *Rhodococcus luteus* depends from the nature used substrate. At growth of bacteria on water-insoluble substrate the culture broth forms emulsions best (E_{24} = 50 %), than at the utilization by microorganisms water-soluble substrate (E_{24} = 10 %) (Tab. 2).

Was studied the dependence of accumulation of biomass and biosurfactants at growth the strain *Rhodococcus luteus* on the mineral salts medium with different concentrations substrates with determination of specific growth rate (μ), max specific growth rate (μ_{max}), constant of affinity the cell to substrate (K_s) at using of the equation Mono and its modifications (Fig. 1,2).

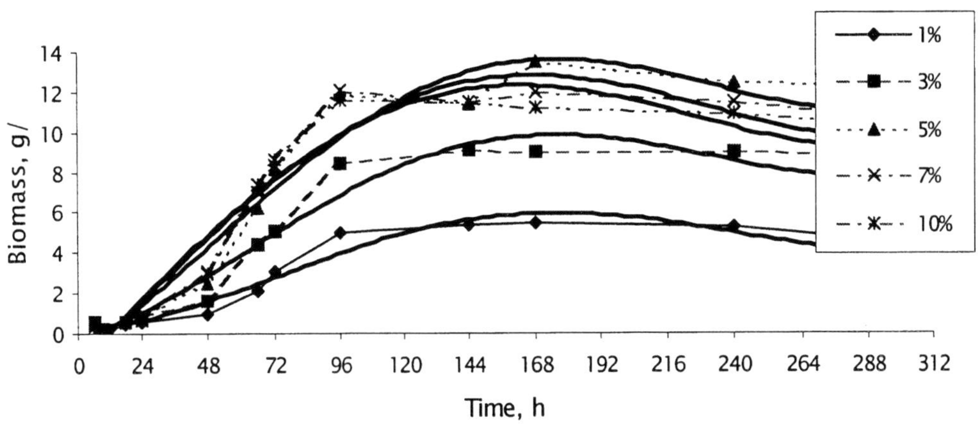

Figure 1. The dependence of accumulation of biomass from time the strain *Rhodococcus luteus* (a sources of carbon and energy – saccharose)

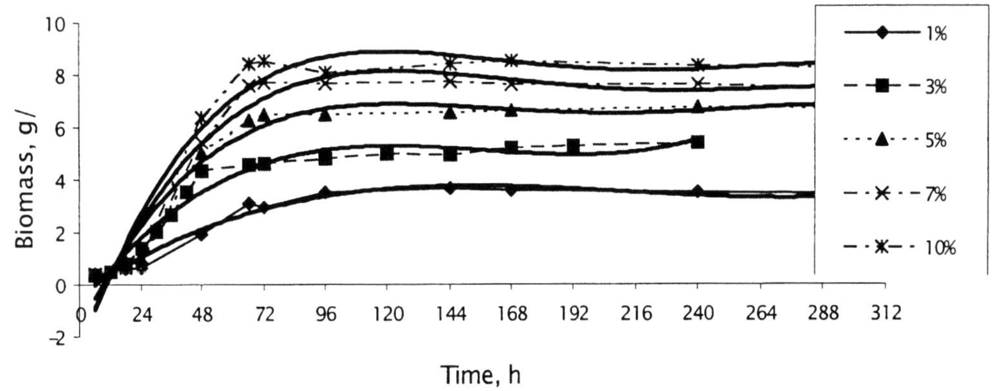

Figure 2. The dependence of accumulation of biomass from time the strain *Rhodococcus luteus* (a sources of carbon and energy – *n*-hexadecane)

The kinetics of growth Rhodococcus luteus in the most active phase of growth - exponential was analysed. We proceeded from the assumption that the process of accumulation of microbial biomass is directly proportional to quantity of cells in the system:

$$M(t) = N_0 * e^{\mu t}, \quad (1)$$

where N_0 - quantity of biomass (g/l) in an initial instant of time.

Is analogously to the equation Michaelis-Menten for kinetics of enzymatic reactions in our case μ_{max} and K_s possibly determine on the basis of linearization of the equation:

$$\mu(S) = \frac{\mu_{\max} * S}{K_s + S} \quad (2)$$

$$\frac{1}{\mu} = \frac{1}{\mu_{\max}} + \frac{K_s}{\mu_{\max}} * S; \quad (3)$$

The specific growth rate (μ) depends from concentration of limiting substrate (S). These equations reflect multi-stage the nature of the process of conversion initial substrate in the product:

$$S + N \rightarrow \begin{matrix} X_n \\ \uparrow\downarrow \\ XS \end{matrix} \rightarrow 2N \quad (4)$$

At that the first stage of the process depends from substrate and the rate of this stage can be regulated by its concentration. For this reason, the values μ increase at raise of concentration of a source of carbon. The second stage does not depend from concentration substrate. This stage limits the process of dividing of bacterial cells. The maximum specific growth rate (μ_{max}) characterises this process (Tab. 3).

Table 3. The dependence of kinetic parameters of growth of the strain *Rhodococcus luteus* from the concentratoin *n*-hexadecane and saccharose in mineral salts medium

Substrate	Saccharose			*n*-Hexadecane		
S_0, %/Vol	μ, h^{-1}	μ_{max}, h^{-1}	K_s, Mol	μ, h^{-1}	μ_{max}, h^{-1}	K_s, Mol
1	0,03666	0,045	0,0006	0,034504	0,056	0,006
3	0,04056	0,045	0,0006	0,041177	0,056	0,006
5	0,0435	0,045	0,0006	0,047212	0,056	0,006
7	0,04424	0,045	0,0006	0,050149	0,056	0,006
10	0,04337	0,045	0,0006	0,052248	0,056	0,006

As is visible, with raise of concentration of substrate (*n*-hexadecane and saccharose) the values of specific growth rate of the strain (μ) are increased and approximate to value of the maximum specific growth rate of bacterial culture (μmax).

In an exponential phase of growth of culture are exhibited different inhibitory effects influencing on specific growth rate. Therefore it is very important to define, what a type of the inhibition is characteristic for the growth of the researched strain. It allows controlling growth of bacteria and, mainly, synthesis by them biosurfactant.

The presence of inhibition and its mechanism can be defined from nature of a curve of growth of bacterial cells. Independently of a type of the inhibition the kinetics of growth formally can describe by one equation [5]:

$$Ln(\frac{M}{N_0}) + \Phi * \frac{M - N_0}{M_{\max}} = \mu t, \qquad (5)$$

where Φ – parameter imaging the mechanism of inhibition. The uncomplicated growth, the inhibition by the product or the inhibition by the substrate can differentiate if to define experimentally values Φ. If $\Phi < 0$, it the inhibition by the substrate; if $0 < \Phi < 1$, we have the uncomplicated growth and if $\Phi > 1$ - the inhibition by products of synthesis.

For definition of parameter Φ for each concentration of n-hexadecane and saccharose was constructed the curve of dependence $\ln(M/N_0)/t$ from $((M-N_0)/M_{max})/t$:

$$Ln(\frac{M_i}{M_j}) / (t_i - t_j) = \mu - \Phi * \frac{M_i - M_j}{(t_i - t_j) M_{\max}} \qquad (6)$$

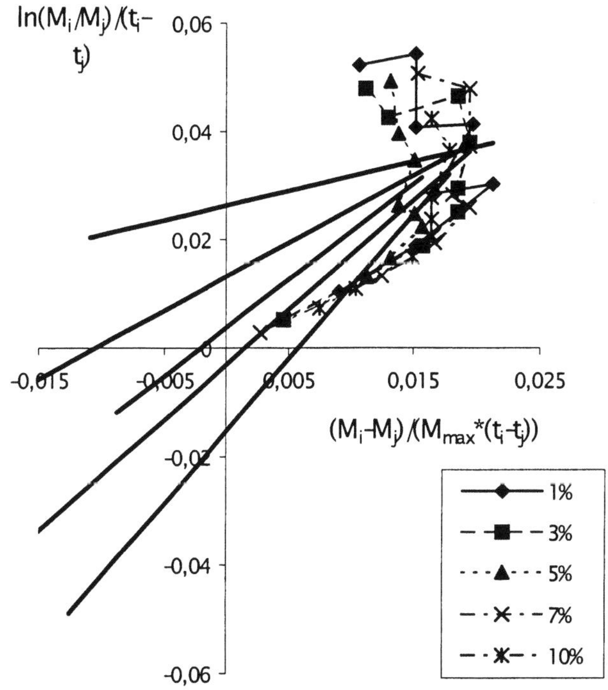

Figure 3. Kinetic curves of growth Rhodococcus luteus on mineral salt medium with different concentration of saccharose (by Eq. (6)).

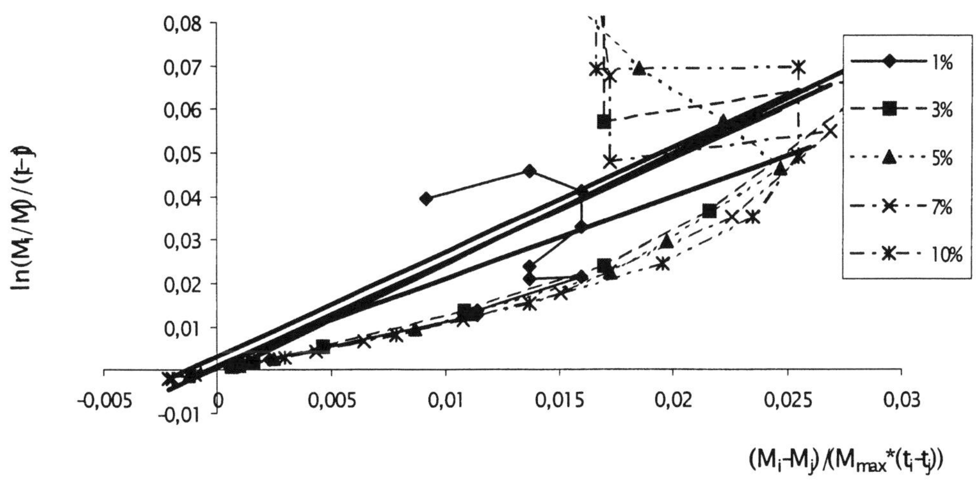

Figure 4. Kinetic curves of growth Rhodococcus luteus on mineral salt medium with different concentration of *n*-hexadecane (by Eq. (6)).

The tangent of slope ratio of this curve defines Φ (fig. 3,4).). These data are exhibited in the table 4.

Table 4. Values of parameter at the growth *Rhodococcus luteus* on saccharose and *n*-hexadecane

Substrate, %/Vol	Saccharose	*n*-Hexadecane
1	0,29	0,38
3	0,65	0,49
5	0,93	0,51
7	1,04	0,51
10	1,38	0,51

In case of using *n*-hexadecane the value of parameter Φ responds the uncomplicated growth ($0 < \Phi < 1$), i.e. growth of culture of bacteria not inhibits neither products of synthesis, nor high concentrations of the substrate. At using saccharose in the mineral salts medium is observed the inhibition by products of synthesis ($\Phi > 1$).

During growth on the mineral salt medium with *n*-hexadecane or saccharose the strain *Rhodococcus luteus* the sufficiently large *lag*-phase is observed. *Lag*-phase has the different nature [5]. It is supposed that the period of induction is tied up with different processes passing in a bacterial cell during growth on different substrate (not fermentative transformation the initial substrate in such product, which one already can be used in further metabolism; adaptive processes in a cell, i.e. synthesis of necessary enzyme or even of the enzymatic system; the presence at the system of inhibitor, concentration which one can be decreased and then the bacterial cells can begin dividing). These main cases can be differentiated on the basis of study of dependence of period of induction (τ) from initial concentration of a source of carbon (S_0). Period of induction (τ) is defined at analysis of an exponential phase of growth in semilogarithmic coordinates out of dependence $\ln(M/N_0)$ from time of cultivating (t) as a segment, which one is cut off on the axis of abscissas at $\ln(M/N_0)=0$ (Fig. 5,6).

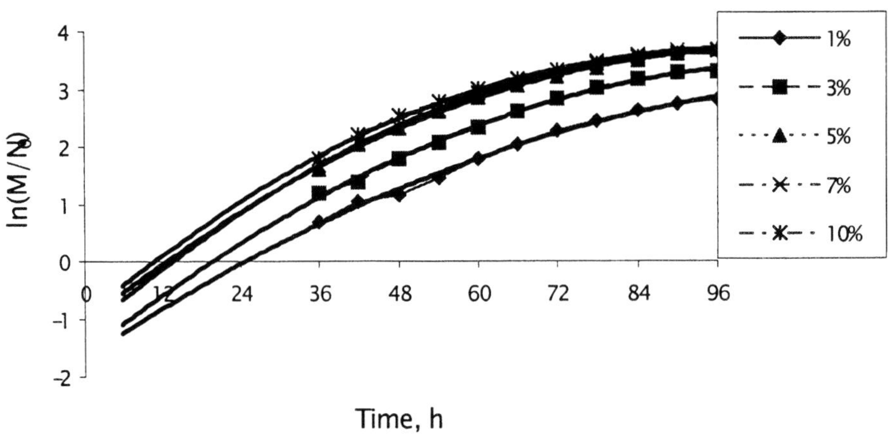

Figure 5. Kinetic curves of growth Rhodococcus luteus on mineral salt medium with different concentration of saccharose in an exponential phase in semilogarithmic coordinates

In case of using saccharose with increase of concentration substrate the period of induction (τ) completely not disappear and simultaneously not approach to constant value (τ= 24; 19,5; 13,5; 13; 11 hours) (Fig. 5 and 6). Presence of period of induction in this case can explain by passing of two important processes in a bacterial cell: conversion presubstrate in substrare and adaptive processes in a bacterial cell. It is known that the bacteria from the genus *Rhodococcus* easier assimilate fructose and glucose, than saccharose. Therefore, for a bacterial cell is necessary some time for synthesis of necessary enzymatic system, which one is using at the assimilation of saccharose. Also simultaneously with this process is passed the splitting of saccharose on fructose and glucose, which one in turn are best substrates for bacteria.

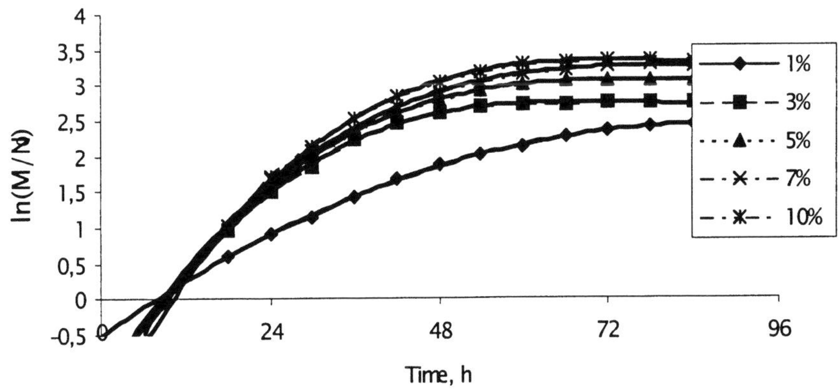

Figure 6. Kinetic curves of growth Rhodococcus luteus on mineral salt medium with different concentration of *n*-hexadecane in an exponential phase in semilogarithmic coordinates

In case of using *n*-hexadecane with increase of concentration substrate the duration of *lag*-period diminishes and simultaneously approaches to constant value (τ =9 hours), that points to the adaptive processes passing in a cell.

Thus, the definition of kinetic parameters of growth of the strain *Rhodococcus luteus* allows controlling synthesis of biosurfactants. Therefore, it is expedient to use concentration substrate not the greater 3 %. The increase of concentrations of *n*-hexadecane or saccharose with presence of processes of inhibition during growth the straine *Rhodococcus luteus* does not give an adequate yield of biomass and biosurfactants in relation to expenses of substrate.

REFERENCES

1. Shulga, A.N., Vildanova-Martsishin, R.I., Shabo, Z.V., Turovsky, A.A. 1991. *Microbiol. J.* **53**, 6. P. 61-66.
2. Karpenko, E.V., Shulga, A.N., Sheglova, N.S., Elyseev, S.A., Vildanova-Martsishin, R.I., Turovsky, A.A. 1996. *Microbiol. J.* **58**, P. 18-24.
3. Koronelli, T.V., Komarova, T.I., Batrakov, S.G. 1990. *Microbiology*. **5**. P. 777-780.
4. M.E. Vogt Singer, W.R. Finnerty. Physiology of biosurfactant synthesis by Rhodococcus species H13-A 1990. *Can. J.Microbiol.* **36**, 11. P. 741-745.
5. Varfolomeev, S.D., Kaljuznyj, S.V. 1990. *High schools*. M. 296 p.
6. *Methods of general bacteriology*. Edited by F.Gerhard etc. 1983. M.: Mir. **1**. 535p.
7. Hommel, R., Stuwer, O., Stuber, W., Haferburg, D., and Kleber, H.-P. 1987. Production of water-soluble surface-active exolipids by Torulopsis apicola. Appl. *Microbiol.and Biotechnol.* **26**. P.199-205.
8. *Biochemical studies of membranes*. Edited by E. Meddi. 1979. M., Mir. 300 p.
9. Ado, Sand Saito, M. *Chromatography lipid, biomedical research and chemical diagnostic*. 1987. Elsevier.: Amsterdames. P.266-310.
10. Alejnikova, T.L., Rubcova, G.V. 1988. M. 132 p.
11. Ambramson, A.A., Bobrovaj, L.E., Zaichenko, L.P. etc. 1984. L. 392 p.
12. Cooper, D.G. and Goldenberg, B.C. 1987. *Appl. and Environm. Microbiol.* **53**. P. 224.

INDEX

#

A

B

C

D

L

M

N

O

P

R

S

T

U

V

W

Y

Z